TEARS, LOVE, LAUGHTER

TEARS, LOVE, LAUGHTER

Celebrating 30 Years of
Arthur Rank House
Cambridge' Hospice

by
Judith Chisholm

with Lucy Day & Annie van Heerden

First published by Arthur Rank Hospice Charity July 2013
Copyright © Judith Chisholm 2013

British Library Cataloguing in Publication Data
Data Available

ISBN 978-0-9926134-0-2

Design by Geraldine Woods
Printed by Victoire Press Ltd
Bar Hill, Cambridge

Published by Arthur Rank Hospice Charity
Arthur Rank House
351 Mill Road, Cambridge CB1 3DF
www.arhc.org.uk
Registered Charity Number 1133354

Preface

We have presented hard facts and figures here and straight history also, but the reader will find that this is a celebration of the creation and work of Arthur Rank House (ARH), the hospice for Cambridge and surrounding area. The picture it presents, of what a hospice is and does, together with the inter-relationship between hospice and the charity underpinning it, is primarily presented through "Voices".

We hope that by letting people speak for themselves in these pages, whether they are users, staff or volunteers, they will also be speaking for everyone else who has been involved with ARH. Using people's voices gives an immediacy that might otherwise be lacking, but also goes to the heart of a basic tenet of hospice care – that we are, each one of us, a unique individual and our voice should be heard.

Were we to attempt to listen to all the voices of all of the people who have been associated with ARH over the 30+ years since its inception, we would be presenting a multi-volume work. So many, named or unnamed, have worked immensely hard and continue to do so. We are all too aware that there are, no doubt, embarrassing omissions of key facts, moments and people, and we apologise if this is felt to be so. However, the voices heard here do represent not only many others, but also, we believe, give a true insight into a special, treasured place and its work.

We dedicate this celebration of Arthur Rank House to users past, present and future and to those who are the enablers of its work.

(Judith Chisholm, Lucy Day and Annie van Heerden, April 2013)

Contents

Definitions: What is a Hospice?

If this is a celebration of 30 years of Arthur Rank House, the hospice for Cambridge and surrounding area, then we should start with a definition, an explanation, of what we understand a hospice to be. And the best place to start is with a talk Dame Cicely Saunders gave in Cambridge in 1981 to mark the beginning of a hospice presence in Cambridge.

Dame Cicely was the founder of St Christopher's, London, and of the whole hospice movement in the UK. In her 1981 Cambridge speech, she offered the following definitions: "Hospice has come to mean an attitude and expertise rather than a specific place". "My own personal definition of what is a hospice: it is a skilled community working to improve the quality of life remaining for patients and families who are struggling with mortal and long-term illness in their midst". The emphasis from the beginning has always been on the quality of life and also on caring for both the patient and the family.

"The word 'hospice' has a long history. It derives from a Latin root meaning both host and guest: it implies interchange, hospitality, giving and receiving. In the Middle Ages, a hospice was a place of refuge providing a place of refreshment for pilgrims and travellers: all were welcomed and sheltered. The philosophy behind the hospice movement remains the same today". Writing this in a Friends of Arthur Rank House Newsletter, Helen Gardner was wanting to highlight the fact that all are welcomed, the ill person and their friends and family, with the hospice aiming to support everyone.

It is important to point out that, as Cicely Saunders said: "There is not only one way out of a Hospice, a considerable number of people are discharged, some of our patients seem to go in and out like yoyos and Hospice in fact means home care as well". This is a very important point since, 30 years on, there is still fear, still a very widespread view held within the community that if you cross the threshold of Arthur Rank House you have, in effect, "turned up your toes", which is absolutely not the case. We hope in the course of this book to dispel some of these fears. It will be seen later that roughly half the beds on the In-Patient Unit are used for symptom control and patients return to their own homes with their quality of life much improved. After 30+ years of ARH, there is an increasing conversation nationally about end-of-life care and individual choice – a key concern for each of us.

Cicely Saunders was clear that: "We did not set out to set up a string of little St Christophers. We set out to be a 'one off' … and to encourage people to do similar work in every which way they could think of". But she would undoubtedly have agreed with Dr Margaret Saunders, current Clinical Director of ARH, that: "Providing a safe place with time to reflect lies at the heart of hospice care". Dr Saunders added: "It must be a little daunting for those new to palliative care and hospice work to sense how 'at ease' the staff (and volunteers) in the service are with the reality of death and dying".

At Arthur Rank House, the whole approach, the whole emphasis is on: "Living well, not waiting to die". Liz Webb (ARH's modern Matron) comments: "Being able to support someone's dying wishes is very compelling". As staff have said: "People have pathways through Arthur Rank House and the fact that someone is coming to the end of life is a given, it's a starting point". People find their own routes through ARH – via Day Therapy, Out Patients, In-Patient symptom control, End-of-Life care, Hospice at Home, Family Support, helped by staff and volunteers, "who always go the extra mile". Hospice care is about taking a holistic approach, finding out what works for an individual: "To do different things for each patient, everyone is different". This lies at the core of hospice care: relief of pain, return of control to the patient, listening, offering time and nurture, support and comfort. Each person's experiences are unique to them.

A Day in the Life of Arthur Rank House: Receptionist's View

I try to get into work a bit earlier than 9am so I can set up the Reception Desk and get a head start on the day.

This morning I'm not surprised to find a box of books, a bag of clothes and a container of children's toys, all donations for our Charity Shops, I presume.

There are numerous notes and bits of paper asking me to arrange transport, a request for a room booking and a light which "needs attention" – there's no indication as to where the light is or what is wrong with the light, just that it needs attention! Let's hope the old psychic powers kick in sometime today!

I am a little taken aback to see what appears to be a pair of beautifully laundered Y-fronts, folded neatly on top of my keyboard. Unfortunately this time, there is no note to advise me why they are there, what to do with them or even who they belong to.

I have worked at Arthur Rank House for almost four years, during which time I have learned to expect the unexpected and so the appearance of a pair of Y-fronts on my desk really shouldn't faze me!

I'm just about to sort out the messages (and the Y-fronts) when I look up to find I am surrounded by people: two couriers needing signatures, a Community Nurse desperately needs a meeting room "NOW", and another member of staff needs the key to the stationery cupboard. Heading in my direction is another colleague who has obviously been fighting with the photocopier as she has black powder on the front of her pink top and a bundle of paper in her hand – and she's not smiling.

After welcoming the first out-patient of the day and making them a cup of tea, I book the meeting room requested, find the much-needed key and un-jam the offending photocopier, assuring my colleague that the machine hates everyone, not just her and get back to my desk just in time to see a flash of yellow outside in the car park. It's an ambulance. We are expecting a new admission to the In-Patient Unit today and it looks like they have arrived.

This is my most favourite part of my job, welcoming patients onto the ward.

People ask me all the time: "How can you work in a place like that? It must be awful, all doom and gloom". It's not like that at all. Yes, we do feel sad and upset if one of our patients passes away because, during the time they are with us, we get to know them, their families and their friends.

A lot of people come into Arthur Rank House to have their pain (caused by their illness) managed or their symptoms alleviated. Once this has been achieved, they are discharged and go home and have a much better quality of life than they had before they came in. I've seen people come in on stretchers and, after the right treatment, have been able to walk out looking like a completely different person! That never, ever ceases to amaze me!

The ambulance crew bring the patient in and I make a point of going around to the front of the desk to welcome him and introduce myself. If I can, I like to accompany the patient round to the ward so they have someone to talk to if the nurses are busy with other patients. Given that some people think ARH is all "doom and gloom", I think it's up to me to try to give them a very different impression. The Ambulance Crew are regulars here and depending on how "well" the patient is and, if it's appropriate, I like to have a little banter with the crew. "Did you have a comfortable journey on the way over, Mr X? Because these two are known as Starsky and Hutch back at the base!" The crew always join in and it's then you see the patient visibly relax. It's so nice to know you have achieved that and dispelled some of the anxiety the patient was obviously feeling.

Once I've seen the patient into the safe hands of our nursing staff, it's back to the desk. Over the course of the day, I have ordered, chased up and sent back to Addenbrooke's stacks of medical records, telephoned staff to warn them of the arrival of the sandwich man and to be quick, sometimes he only stays for 0.3 seconds, booked numerous meeting rooms, greeted many visitors, almost reported a dripping tap, ordered two taxis, arranged eight lots of ambulance transport, re-directed a foreign (confused) visitor to the dentist in the next street and answered hundreds of phone calls in between.

Over the course of the day, our wonderful Tea Bar volunteers make me cups of tea and ply me with home-made cake. There's no danger of me wasting away to size zero at Arthur Rank House!

(Shelagh van Heerden, March 2013)

Palliative Medicine Practitioner: Consultant Doctor

Currently, the role of Consultant involves combining being the Consultant in Palliative Care at Papworth Hospital, together with being the Clinical Director for Arthur Rank House.

During the past decade or so, Arthur Rank House has become more outward facing. As a result, the work of the Senior Consultant now includes:

- Clinical Director role
- Advisory and supervisory
- Hearing about patients from others and asking questions
- Helping people analyse situations and make decisions
- Helping to integrate individuals' knowledge
- Liaising with other hospitals and GPs
- Responsibilities for domiciliary services and support therapists
- Planning strategic work
- Education – medical students (NB any clinical discussion is educational for those taking part)
- Reviewing services

(in addition to patient care and management!)

Personal View - Dr Margaret Saunders

Palliative care is not protocol-driven. We do things so differently for each individual. Patients we work with are willing to try anything. It makes you into Sherlock Holmes, always looking for a little clue, which is why it can be so unnerving to hospital colleagues who expect a + b = c and will be the same next time. It's so personal, so challenging and intense, integrating observations, listening to what's happening, that it's difficult for the precise treatment for one patient to have validity for others.

The non-pharmacological approach is integrated with medical pharmacology. We have constantly to come up with new ideas to treat that person. As the starting point, one needs to be a very good physician to assess well clinically. We mix medical science with so much non-medical/non-pharmacological discussion. It is a process of analysing the problem, integrating all the information, talking to the patients and having a shared understanding of what's good for them. It is very alien to modern medicine.

I'm often asked: 'Is it very depressing?' and the answer is: 'It's very sad, but the reality is that if I were to become depressed I could not be useful'. There is a sadness we feel for the patient and the family. The fact that someone is coming towards the end of their life is a given – it is a starting point.

It is a privilege working with people at this time of their lives. People share things with us, there is no need or requirement, and that allows us to share such an important part of their lives. How much we value that, and the learning that goes on. I just learn so much every day – it's a constant joy, the element of constant discovery and shared learning with the patient. There is so much joy in what we do.

Brief Biography

Dr Saunders started as an anaesthetist – they also practise pain relief – and found in that work, together with intensive care, she encountered every need of the patient and their family –meeting the whole person. From there she moved into palliative care. It was a somewhat difficult transition from the normal hospital hierarchy but she learnt: "we're all equal partners" at ARH. She always says to people who want to work in palliative care that: "You don't need a religious faith, but you do need to have a philosophy of life".

Dame Cicely Saunders

A brief biographical sketch of Cicely Saunders' work reveals how extraordinarily innovative she was and how actively her legacy is at work today, which is why we are including this piece here about her and her support for Arthur Rank House. Her brother, Christopher Saunders, in a 2012 talk to Cambridge U3A, said her work begun in the 1940s has resulted in there now being hospice and care teams in 136 countries, while in the UK there are 223 adult hospices and 43 for children.

Cicely Saunders' lifelong commitment to caring for people began in 1940 when she abandoned her Oxford degree course in Politics, Philosophy and Economics (PPE) to go to London and train as a nurse. In 1944, she returned to Oxford and within a year had completed her PPE degree and gained a diploma in public health.

As a medical social worker, she had a profound encounter with a young Polish Jew, David Tasma, who was dying of cancer. This was to change her life. Through this friendship and her increasingly profound concern for the lack of appropriate care for the dying she was witnessing, she felt a calling to devote her life to this then most neglected group.

As she said in her Cambridge talk in 1981: "It all began because I was left £500 by a patient who said, 'I'll be a window in your home'. I was at that time a medical social worker. It took me 19 years to build a home round the window – as I did have to go and read medicine to do something about it". Though Cicely herself said: "There are not many original ideas in the world and what needed to happen was a whole lot of ideas gradually to come together into a new pattern. Having put those ideas together, it was in a sense like putting them into a kaleidoscope, giving it a shake and letting it fall down into a new pattern". This seriously underplays her vision.

With the opening of St Christopher's Hospice in London in 1967: "she brought together for the first time in the world, a large number of patients with terminal illness and staff who were committed to discover and then teach the best ways of caring for them. Previously these patients would have been scattered – in various hospital wards or at home. There were a few hospices, mostly opened around 1900. The patients in them received excellent nursing and spiritual care but there was minimal medical input, for it was generally believed that the doctor's role was to cure".

This description comes from Dr Mary Baines who, having met Cicely Saunders when they were medical students together, was recruited by her to join St Christopher's. As she says of that moment: "I found myself entering a branch of medicine with no books or conferences. Symptom control was contained in a single sheet entitled 'Drugs most commonly used at St Christopher's Hospice', which was given to all staff. Yet, I suggest, this sheet contains the single most important advance in end-of-life care that has ever been made".

What Dr Baines is referring to here is Cicely's revolutionary discovery of how to control pain in terminal illness. Through her observations and research, she established the basic pattern of pain control that exists today: "of giving a strong opioid by mouth, regularly and in adequate doses" so people can be both pain-free and remain alert.

Equally revolutionary was Cicely's concept of "total pain". Even before the opening of St Christopher's, she had written of there being four components to "total pain": physical, emotional, social and spiritual. As Christopher Saunders pointed out, if one pays attention to all four factors and is "seeing the patient as a whole", it is often possible to use lower doses of conventional opioid pain relief. The time to spend with patients – to talk and to listen is of great importance.

As with Arthur Rank House, Cicely Saunders extended hospice care to those living in their own homes, starting this service in 1969.

In her Cambridge speech, Cicely Saunders said: "There is a whole series of elements that came together to form the first research and teaching hospice, which was St Christopher's". This emphasis on both research and teaching was key to the impact she has had. Christopher Saunders remembers being told by a doctor his sister worked for while preparing to establish St Christopher's, that she claimed "It's the doctors who desert the dying". Her colleague Dr Baines is clear that: "There is no doubt that Cicely Saunders did not found St Christopher's purely to care for patients in south-east London. Her aim was to change the world's view of dying and this aim was shared by those who worked with her".

We hope that through this brief sketch of the work of Cicely Saunders it can be seen how she did indeed bring about a revolution – how she founded palliative care and how doctors within this area embrace those people whom they can no longer cure but can help them live well. Through looking at what was so revolutionary, we can better understand the work of Arthur Rank House today.

Continuing the Commitment: A Trustee

Kate Kirk got involved with hospice work because it runs in the family – she is Cicely Saunders' niece. Her three older cousins had all done their summer stint helping at St Christopher's, so after her A Levels, Kate also volunteered. At that time, St Christopher's ran a four-to-six-week summer volunteer programme. "Basically I was an auxiliary nurse. Accommodation was provided and we worked shifts. I was with an interesting bunch of people, an Israeli doctor, a German nurse and seven or eight other people. I was the only non-medical one". Dame Cicely (who had very piercing eyes) was very keen on education and keen to draw people to her to see how palliative care worked and then go back into their own communities to carry forward this type of care as best suited their context.

Now, as a trustee of the Arthur Rank Hospice Charity, Kate finds that being involved with the hospice and with the charity brings so many people together, from so many parts of life. "It restores your faith in people" to have all helping in different ways. "It is more than the sum of its parts – it's a community in miniature".

Patient Voice: In-Patient Unit - Dennis

I was an in-patient at Arthur Rank House and the care was just wonderful, no words can describe how they looked after me. I could not have wanted better care, everyone I came into contact with just wanted to help you.
(Dennis)

The Class of '81: Photo and Comments

Caring

Dignity

Couldn't wish for a nicer place

Mixture of emotions

Happy place to work

Staff support each other, as well as patients and loved ones

Calm – when you walk through the door there is an immediate feeling of calm

Strength (needed when times feel dark)

Reflection – bi-annual Reflection sessions for loved ones: you sensed they were pleased to come back, it made you (staff) realise you'd done something special

At Reflection sessions, staff weren't in uniform – it was important that we were seen as "people"

Refreshing – one could care for people as one wanted to, in all aspects – the whole self

Liberating – for staff and patients. Staff could use old "things" in new ways. We were innovative in the way we could deliver treatment. Patients – we did what the patients and their loved ones wanted.

No Rules – if it worked, you did it

Homely – felt comfortable

Feeling of community

Flexibility – it was the early days of the Hospice movement, and it was great, we were there to give emotional as well as physical comfort

Unconventional – champagne, pets, own space – whatever patients wanted!

The Pioneers – Class of '81

(Back Row from Left)
Ann Murray, Caroline Bacon, Rosemary Harrison, Pam Wadham,
Esmee Young, Sheena Henderson

(Front Row from Left)
Jeanette Orloff, Trudy Garner, Joan Reeds, Ann Cooper, Doreen Rees,
Kathy Hines, Janet McCabe

Founding Hospice Care in Cambridge:
Arthur Rank House

We have seen how Cicely Saunders worked to establish St Christopher's Hospice in London and how she developed palliative care and founded what we know today as the hospice movement. Within Cambridge itself, there was increasing discussion during the 1970s about the need for some kind of hospice provision locally.

Not surprisingly, people looked to St Christopher's and Cicely Saunders to explore what a hospice is, might be and what would fit locally. The Cambridge Evening News of 29 January 1976 reported on such a visit to St Christopher's. It also noted that Peterborough rejected the idea of a hospice there on the grounds that: "Doctors there have said they think the right place for the dying is in their own home". Of course now, this is not seen as an "either/or" but as a matter of individual choice. Nor is a hospice now seen as solely being a place where one only goes to die, though there are still too many people who have this impression. These changes are critical markers in how far the journey has been during the past 30+ years.

A growing number of people began to push to have a hospice in Cambridge. With the support of the then Regius Professor of Physic, J.S. Mitchell, a small committee of interested people was set up under the chairmanship of Lady Todd. As Joan Porter (who had been Sister in Charge of Addenbrooke's Hospital Radiotherapy Centre) wrote: "We knew that a huge sum would be required (£1/2m.), but we could start to stimulate public interest by running a variety of fund-raising events: concerts, coffee mornings, auctions, fashion parades etc". Dr David Bratherton, a therapeutic radiologist at Addenbrooke's Hospital, was also very influential in moving the project forward (see Milestone: The First 36 Months). As with so many others, he was also inspired by the work at St Christopher's and knew that somewhere other than hospital wards needed to be provided for the terminally ill. He was to become the first Medical Director of the new hospice.

The site of Brookfields (where there had been a hospital since 1883) was chosen for the new hospice, for Continuing Care as it was known by the Health Authority. Momentum for fundraising gathered pace. Meanwhile, a National Appeal was launched under the Chairmanship of Sir Francis Pemberton, sponsored by the National Society for Cancer Relief and by the

Cambridge Area Health Authority. Together, the J. Arthur Rank Group of Charities – hence the name – provided £200,000 and the Cambridge Cancer Relief Appeal provided matching funds. The remainder of the £530,000 was provided by the Health Authority. Sheila Hancock cut the first sod in 1979 and the completed building was handed over on 5 May 1981 with the first patients admitted soon after. On 15 October 1981, Arthur Rank House was officially opened by the President of the National Society for Cancer Relief, the Duchess of Kent.

Very shortly after, the association of Friends of Arthur Rank House and Brookfields Hospital was established with Christine McCrum as its first Chair. The Friends Committee quickly became an important support for the hospice, not least as a means of publicising the work of ARH, raising funds to further its development and encouraging volunteers. Thus began the fruitful relationship and inter-relationship which can be seen today between the work of Arthur Rank House and that of the Arthur Rank Hospice Charity.

Patient Voice: Ann's Story

For anyone who knew and loved Ann, they would recognise that it would be typical of her that, as she lay dying in Arthur Rank House, she would write a letter to the local paper, the Cambridge News, expressing her gratitude for the care she was receiving at the Hospice.

For anyone who knows Arthur Rank House, they would know that it was typical of the hospice that they would receive Ann from a hospital ward where they had been unable to control her pain and that, within 24 hours, they would have found a way of controlling this pain and thus liberating her. So, as Ann lay dying, ARH supported and facilitated her. She worked with her friends and instructed them on how to complete her last project – a book on the trees of The Botanic Garden in Cambridge. Ann had embarked on this book because of her love of, and interest in, trees, and because she was no longer able to travel far.

So lucky to be in this hospice

I WAS diagnosed with jaw cancer in 2001. Since then I have been looked after very well indeed by the NHS: surgery (more than once), radiotherapy and chemotherapy. The NHS has given me some good years.

I was managing well until suddenly, four weeks ago, I was in intolerable pain. An ambulance took me to Addenbrooke's, where the palliative care specialists did all they could for me.

Then, thankfully, a bed was found for me at the Arthur Rank Hospice. I am so lucky to be here: the staff are kind and gentle and patient, and they make sure that I am never in pain. Nothing is too much trouble for them.

There is a lovely, family atmosphere at the hospice, for me and for the friends who visit me here. We are so fortunate to have such a facility in Cambridge. Long may it continue to give wonderful care to those who can no longer look after themselves.

Ann Johnston
Covent Garden
Cambridge

Palliative Care: Nurse Manager, In-Patient Unit

Use the word "hospice", mention Arthur Rank House, and one is constantly meeting the misconception that it is a place where once you've crossed the threshold, you don't come back. In fact, the In-Patient Unit (IPU) is used as much for symptom control as it is for end-of-life care.

When Arthur Rank House first opened, it was used only for in-patient care and those 25 beds could often be occupied for weeks, even months, at a time by the same person. The pattern is radically different now. There are fewer beds and bed occupancy is roughly 50% for end-of-life care and 50% for symptom control. There is a lot more use of the IPU for symptom control than formerly, partly because patients are living longer with their illnesses. There is also more patient choice. Additionally, IPU now witnesses a shorter end-of-life stay, partly because choices can be made for short stay and partly because there are more community-based resources.

The IPU has a less obvious but critical role in that it is the only service that is 24/7 – so patients and GPs telephone, seeking advice. It is the only resource available. Often it is just a matter of giving reassurance during "out of hours".

Carly Love is the current IPU manager. Despite her many responsibilities for the unit as a whole, she tries to ensure that she also works clinically as a nurse.

The Manager's job includes being responsible for nursing staff, recruitment, education, rota, budget, ordering stores, trying to develop the service and clinical supervision.

Of prime importance is looking at ways in which the In-Patient Unit meets patient needs, of developing links with other services outside ARH and at patient transitions back into the community, as well as promoting the services ARH offers.

As with so many other staff and volunteer members of ARH, Carly is very aware and appreciative of how she receives support "from everyone in the building". Everyone within Arthur Rank House, including the domestic staff, are "absorbing" what goes on and so all are involved with the patients and with the family support, which is very important. Anyone can call a "debrief" with the staff. In addition, there is now formal clinical supervision for staff. This session, every 6–8 weeks, allows for "celebration of the good" as well as looking at whatever issues may crop up.

Carly is clear that it is important to "try to de-hospitalise IPU as much as we can". Helping her in this goal for a while was Black Cat. No-one knows how he was "acquired" but the cat kept coming and "made it his home". He would wander around Day Therapy and sit on patients' beds. If shooed away he would never try again, only going where he was appreciated and he always slept away from the clinical unit. Carly can remember seeing Black Cat being pulled round by his tail by a patient's grandchildren – without complaining. He was a "great de-stresser" for staff and he should have a successor.

Brief Biography

Carly Love came to ARH nine years ago as a staff nurse from Addenbrooke's Hospital. She's a Cambridge lass and had an uncle die at ARH when she was 17. She always wanted to be a nurse from the moment she fell off a coffee table aged five or six and broke her arm. She finds ARH "a great place to work, you feel supported and can say what you're thinking".

Christmas Cat

One Christmas there was a phone call to the In-Patient Unit from the daughter of a patient. She was asking if she could spend Christmas with her mother. 'Of course, there will be a bed for you and you can both be together'. Some time later, the daughter rang again, in considerable distress – she couldn't find anyone to look after her cat. 'Don't worry, that's not a problem. It's simple, bring your cat with you and we can find a private space for the three of you.' So mother, daughter and cat spent that Christmas, together, in the hospice.

Patient Voice: In-Patient Unit - Anon

It's hard in a way because you haven't got much to measure it by, not having been in a situation like this before, but I think one of the first impressions you get is of coming into a happy place, it's not dour or glum or gloomy, people are pleasant, they smile and are welcoming and they laugh. You don't have to feel that just because it's a place where people die or are very poorly that has to be reflected in the attitude here and I think that's absolutely wonderful, I really, really do. And it's the whole person, the whole family, the whole group of you that come in that is cared for. If my daughters need to speak to somebody, there's somebody there to speak to. If I'm concerned about something, there's someone there to listen to me. To feel that you're paramount is a most novel feeling for me as it is I suppose for anyone, not necessarily just for a woman, but women care, they are carers, they are always the ones thinking, even when they are feeling absolutely dreadful, they've still got to get their daughters' lunch for school, make sure they have the things they need, money for such and such, all this sort of thing has to be sorted out. So when somebody cares for you and what are your needs, it's a wonderful freeing, you're allowed to feel rotten.

You're allowed to feel sad, you're allowed to feel happy; all these emotions are legitimate, it gives a legitimacy to who you are and what you are doing. This ethos when you come in is something I feel and that doesn't happen overnight and it's not just one person, it's all the staff who have this awareness of their patients and what is good for one is not necessarily right for another. Every little foible of mine is met; to wanting to have my own butter to put on my cold toast so that it doesn't soak into the toast, even that is thought of. You know it's silly little things like that which make me smile.

The doctors hardly say a word - they let me say all the words. I feel as if I'm yakking on and I think: 'Oh, goodness, perhaps I shouldn't be saying too much, they should be asking me things'; but they want to know how I am and take the time to assess what is the progress of my disease, how they can ease that and I find that very, very comforting.

The relief, absolute relief when they said your needs are paramount and you have to be where it's best for you and you can be here where you can be looked after for as long as you need to be looked after. And that worry and concern just fell away because I realised I had to accept that I couldn't go home and I also had to accept that I was happy about that. (Anon)

Palliative Care: Young Doctor, In-Patient Unit

As a young doctor, Core Medical Trainee level 2 – or Senior House Doctor – a title more people would recognise, Will Brown is working towards becoming a consultant neurologist. As an academic SHO, he has been able to choose this placement. His choice has, in large part, been determined by his understanding that since so much of neurology is not curable, it is necessary to learn: "How to facilitate a good death and how to control symptoms".

During the very first term of his training at Norwich to become a doctor, students had a "death week", which included time with a recently bereaved family. He found it: "Very moving for a 17 year-old rugby player, probably still hungover. It kindled, reiterated why I want to help people, even if it is not possible to cure them". He is very conscious of his father's approach (also a doctor) of the importance of: "Making someone feel better for your presence, rather than what you may do".

Working in Arthur Rank House after Addenbrooke's Hospital has meant a considerable change for Will. Instead of a day-to-day caseload of maybe 15 patients, he is able to see just a small number of patients. "Any doctor wants to spend time with the patients, you can practise medicine as you want to, make sure the nurses are OK, help relatives". A couple of days before Will was interviewed, he saw two people on the IPU. He spent about 10 minutes with the first person but about four hours with the second person. The patient was not at the end of his life, but was very anxious. Rather than "filling him up with drugs", they "chatted things through" and Will was able to relieve the person's anxieties.

One of the main differences Will has found working at ARH is the different ethos, with the aim of treatment being different. Like Dr Saunders, he has encountered the underlying sense from many hospital doctors of: "I do not like to let go" of patients, to acknowledge that they can be best helped by being cared for by palliative care specialists. However, he thinks that the more palliative care for those who are not at the stage of end of life is promoted, the easier it should become for patients to get the best care. For example, patient lymphoedema can best be managed when there is a clear source of expertise as there is in the ARH lymphoedema clinic (see separate section).

Will has been amazed by the ARH nurses. It is not just that he finds that they are technically excellent, but is also aware of how comforting they are to patients and their friends and family. The young nurses and also the student nurses at ARH can have a major input. *(Interviewed February 2013)*

Seeking Advice

My brother was dying in South Africa. I was about to fly out for what I thought would be my last chance to see him. I knew he was terminally ill and I knew he was suffering from extreme breathlessness. I did not know how I could help him. A friend suggested I telephone Arthur Rank House to see if they could offer any advice and suggested a few names of people to contact there.

It was a Friday afternoon last October when I tried phoning and it was hard to reach the people who had been mentioned to me, but I was put through to a ward where someone agreed to speak to me when I explained the position. She was extremely sympathetic and kind and told me it would be very difficult. She suggested getting a hand-held fan and explained why that would be useful. We also discussed the other forms of medical treatment likely to be helpful, and why they were used.

I searched high and low for the hand-held fan, but eventually found one in the travel section of Boots at the airport (I've since seen some in Mark and Spencers!)

The fan was very helpful, as Neil became breathless at the slightest movement and the circulation of air around his face gave a sense of relief. The suggested medication was also exceptionally useful in diminishing the anxiety associated with his breathlessness. Having had the chat before leaving Cambridge made all the difference, as there was no palliative care when I got to Durban. My brother's oncologist came to see him and said, with me present, that he could offer him no further treatment.

I had been given enough information during my phone conversation that I was able to ask the oncologist to prescribe the necessary medication to provide basic palliative care for Neil. The Durban hospice had been involved a few months before, but since they had had no recent contact, had discharged my brother from their list. When I contacted them, they could not do an assessment for some days. When they did come, they explained that they would only visit once a week. The family had to cope themselves, or pay for agency nurses – a totally different experience to that provided by Arthur Rank House!

I was so anxious and stressed when I phoned Arthur Rank House that Friday afternoon before I caught my flight that I never asked the name of the person I talked to on the ward and who gave me so much practical help and support. I would like to take this opportunity of expressing my thanks now.
(C.C., April 2013)

Spirituality

The World Health Organization says that: "It is an incomplete view of humanity which concentrates on the physical, psychological and social but ignores the search for meaning and value which makes up the spiritual element of human living". There is a fundamental difference between "spiritual" and "religious" – some people do put their spirituality into a religious framework, which needs to be respected – for others it is less defined, though no less important. "Spirituality" relates to the basic questions "Who am I?" and "What makes me who I am?"

"Courage consists in equality to the problem before us", wrote R.W. Emerson, the American philosopher.

"Patients and families, faced with terminal illness, have problems before them; their courage is so often equal to those problems.

One can be matter-of-fact about this virtue – patients sometimes say "What can I do except face reality?" – but the whole answer does not lie there. There is something in the human spirit, something in the lives of men and women, committed or not committed to a religious faith, which is evident in these situations. .....

All of us who minister to the courageous, staff, loved ones, and friends, need courage too. We are helped when we see it in someone with whom we share our work. Being prepared to go into the unknown with a patient, to hold a hand in the dark, to be, alas, answerless but to be there. There can be much strength when two or more people are being brave together, not just one".

(Brother Edgar,
First ARH Chaplain)

Longest-Serving Nurse

Trudy Garner joined the team as an auxiliary nurse way back in 1981 not long after the unit first opened. Now talking 30 years later, she continues to love her work and to be inspired by both the aims and working practices of her employment. She is especially fond of the peace found at Arthur Rank House as well as the comradeship felt between all those who work there. Trudy says: "It is a real privilege to care for people and give support at such times of crisis".

As the longest-serving nurse at the hospice, Trudy has naturally seen many changes over her 30 years of happy service. She certainly considers that a good sense of humour has been vital over such a long career.

Apart from memories of weddings and christenings taking place in the hospice, Trudy wanted to recall one special Christmas. "It was Christmas morning a couple of years ago and I was on an early shift. After general handover, I went round the wards wishing all the patients Merry Christmas. I came to a little 90-year-old lady who had arrived late the previous evening and she promptly burst into tears. Because of the shortage of staff over the Christmas period, her district nurses had suggested that she come into Arthur Rank House for that period. I asked her why she was crying and she replied, 'I have nobody. I have been taken from my own house and put here'. I sat on her bed, held her hand and told her that she did have somebody. We, the nurses, were here for her and I personally would look after her that morning and would share Christmas lunch with her. She smiled and continued to hold my hand.

I kept my promise and made her look and feel lovely. We helped her eat her lunch, pulled crackers, put Christmas hats on and read silly jokes. We talked of Christmases past and opened the small bag of presents which "Santa" had left her. Although she was the only patient in her bay, all the nurses made sure she was not alone that Christmas. My experience of that day was that, for such a small gift of my time, so much had been given back to me from a special person. I had been given the joy, happiness, tears and love that cannot be bought, from a dear lady and a stranger who had become my friend by the time my shift had finished. That heartfelt feeling is what makes working at Arthur Rank House so very special and it remains a priceless memory. Although that lady died only two days later, when she had felt most alone, she was in fact surrounded by loving support".

(Adapted from an interview with John Marshall in 2011 –J.C., March 2013)

Trudy

Trudy worked at Arthur Rank House for 31 years. She was an irreplaceable character who wore her heart on her sleeve; this story she tells of Christmas with a patient reflects her caring, practical attitude to her role. She had a very "carpe diem" approach to life and the challenges it raised for her and the patients and staff she worked with over the years. Trudy would recount stories of staff she had "taught" on their first days at Arthur Rank who were now in very senior roles in the NHS. She would say to me, "you know so and so, I taught them everything they know, and now they are a Director of Nursing!" – said with a wry smile and a laugh.

Unfortunately, after a short illness, Trudy was to experience being "surrounded by the love and support" she describes in her story and she died here in May 2013, cared for by her colleagues and friends, an experience that those involved found both a privilege and a challenge. She will be missed in many ways but always remembered as part of Arthur Rank's wide and varied alumni of staff and patients.

(Liz Webb, Matron/Head of Palliative Care Services May 2013)

A Visitor's View

It was December 2009, extremely cold and the Mill Road pavements were icy. But once inside Arthur Rank House, the atmosphere was warm and welcoming. A smile from the receptionist, sign the visitors' book, make our way down the corridor to A's room with flowers and a view of the garden beyond. Ignore the tubes and drips and just chat the way we always used to. Sometimes we read a message from close friends abroad, sometimes we were given – half apologetically – a list of requests. But above all, we talked and laughed. While we were with her beside her bed, it all felt almost normal. It was only as we left that we sensed "I might never see her again". In fact, her stay was longer than that of most patients and she joked about that too. She wrote in an email to us all: "As you can imagine, it is very frustrating that I am not able to slip away quietly (I am too tough)". That was utterly characteristic of her. The care she received was exemplary. One of her last pieces of writing was a letter to the Cambridge Evening News to praise the staff and express her thanks. We knew that she was free of pain, but more importantly, she was calm and free of fear: that made it so much easier for all of us.

Then it was Christmas week. We worried about her but when I saw her for the last time on 31 December, she showed me joyfully a long list of all the visitors who had been to see her over Christmas. By now she was no longer propped up, but lying on her side and her speech had become much harder to make out. But her indomitable spirit was still there and remained to the very end. She died calmly and peacefully, with a nurse beside her, two days later, not alone and not afraid. She was an inspiration to us all.

(J.B., March 2013)

Pioneering Days: The First Physiotherapist

Arthur Rank House was newly established when Rosemary Harrison was a part-time physiotherapist at Addenbrooke's Hospital. One Friday, she recalls, she was called to her manager who told her that on the following Monday morning, she would be working at Arthur Rank House. Having replied that she did not want to go to Arthur Rank House, Rosemary was simply told that her contract required her to work wherever she was sent and that ARH was where she was being sent! She had come to specialise in helping stroke and head-injured patients and felt she had no understanding of what hospice patients would need. However, she was reassured to be told that after a six-month stint at the hospice she would return to hospital-based physiotherapy.

Rosemary recalls that she cried all through the weekend and all the way to her first morning's work at Arthur Rank House. Here she found herself working with Gillian, the occupational therapist. They found they worked very well together, devising their own programmes for supporting the hospice patients. After four of her six months working at ARH, Rosemary realised that she was really enjoying her work and that "everyone was so lovely". In fact, when Rosemary received a call from her manager telling her that she had to return to Addenbrooke's Hospital, she refused. Told once more that she did not have the power to refuse, Rosemary went to Dr Tim Hunt *(Medical Director ARH)* and told him about her problem. He replied that she should not worry. And thereafter there was never again any mention of her leaving ARH!

Rosemary stayed at the hospice for 18 years in all. She says she "learnt a lot about human beings, a lot of good when you don't always expect it". When a patient was going to be discharged, Rosemary and Gillian used to do a joint home visit, one with the patient in one room and the other with a family member in another. This gave people the freedom to share their worries. "It all came out". As with patients in Arthur Rank House, Rosemary found she would be told things that would not necessarily have been confided in doctors or nurses. "We had some good laughs and some good conversations".

Expansion of Arthur Rank House: Establishing Day Therapy

A key stage in the extension of provision of care at Arthur Rank House was the decision to set up a Day Centre. The history of ARH shows that once a goal has been achieved, in the first instance establishing the hospice itself, quite quickly thereafter another area of need is identified – in this case, provision of day care – and then momentum builds towards achieving this new goal.

Today, the Day Therapy service at Arthur Rank House provides specialist advice and support for adults with life-limiting illness. The aim of the service is to enable people to live their lives to the full. The focus is on patient choice and quality of life.

Desire for day therapy provision was identified in the mid 1980s, but took considerable time to achieve. In July 1990, Dr Bernard Reiss, Chairman of the Friends of Arthur Rank House, wrote in the Newsletter: "A day-centre has been suggested in the past and the Friends have long expected a request (from the Health Authority) for help in setting it up and in supporting its day-to-day work. ... One can only dream of a situation in which there is a day-centre".

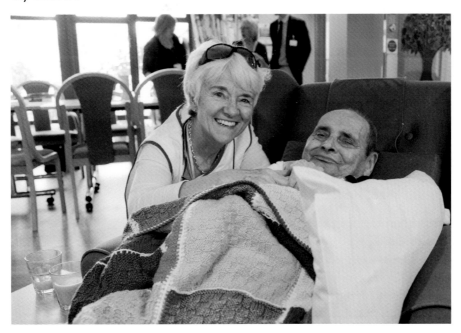

A pilot project was established and then, in 1993, a £1 million appeal was launched by Cancer Relief Macmillan Fund together with Friends of Arthur Rank House. As Penny Cleobury says (see "Memories of a Fundraiser"), "Everyone thinks a hospice is a good thing", so that, remarkably, the centre was built within two years of starting the appeal. The centre is named after Dr Bernard Reiss, the first Director of GP Studies at the Clinical School of Medicine, Cambridge University. It opened in June 1995.

Sheila Walton, Palliative Care Manager writing in the Friends Newsletter, described its significance as follows: "This brought together for the first time all the Palliative Care Services under one roof instead of in different buildings, albeit on the Brookfields Hospital site – the Macmillan team, Marie Curie home nursing, administration, physiotherapy, occupational therapy, day care and Hospital-at-home previously with 'no fixed abode'".

With the official opening of the Day Centre, as it was then called, in September 1995, another building block of the hospice was in place. The extensive work of Day Therapy is explored more fully in subsequent sections.

Fundraising for the Day Centre: Memories of a Fundraiser

In answer to the question "How did it all begin?", Penny explained that she was already a member of the local Cancer Relief Macmillan Fund Committee. At one committee meeting, the then chairman explained that Arthur Rank House wanted a Day Therapy Centre and that it had been agreed that funding for the building would come half from Macmillan and half from Friends of Arthur Rank House. Jean Rogers, the local Macmillan fundraiser, would work on this project but it was agreed that an Events Co-ordinator was needed. Penny says she had no idea what "Events Co-ordinator" meant but thought it sounded interesting, so she volunteered.

The Arthur Rank House Friends' Committee was chaired by Ann Mathias with Eustace Crawley as the deputy – this gave a good City-County balance and contacts network. Jean was given a caravan parked on the Brookfields site as her HQ and Penny's job was "to keep a giant diary". Of course it became much more than this – organising balls, concerts etc. Penny remembers regular meetings, well run and that it was a "very enjoyable time". One of

her main responsibilities was to attend meetings on behalf of Jean Rogers and ensure that expenses were controlled and proportionate to the specific fundraising activity.

"Everyone thinks a hospice is a good thing – it resonated with me to have a centre, to go for a day, to talk openly and share experiences and give a carer time off". "Therapies – start an interest, to help someone feel good about themselves". The project meant, for her, "Interaction with such lovely people, there's so much rubbish in the world but so much goodness".

After the success of helping to raise £1 million within two years, Penny again concentrated her activities with Macmillan Cancer Relief.

Asked what qualities are needed to be a good fundraiser, Penny replied: "A loud voice, a sense of humour, making more money than one spends and getting a group of people who can work together, despite their differences, for a common cause". A friend of hers would add: "Great attention to detail and planning ahead for the unforeseen".

(Penny Cleobury)

Patient Voice: Day Therapy - Clive

I didn't know what to think, before coming to Day Therapy.

My favourite aspect is the therapy; anything therapeutic is good so that's why I come.

What were your expectations?

Medical people referred me, so I expected medical 'intervention' – apart from that I didn't know what to think.

I don't think I would have been keener to attend if I knew more about what was here. I just accepted what was advised.

Is there anything you dislike?

No, I don't feel pushed and feel that everything that happens is done by your own free will.

My favourite part is meeting people to talk with. It also helps listening. I've had complementary therapy on my feet and on my shoulders once.

I've been to the breathlessness clinic a couple of times and the relaxation sessions with Mara helped.

I'm a bit sad I'm leaving today, but I knew it wasn't going to last forever. (Clive)

What is Day Therapy for? Team Leader Explains

The Day Therapy service at Arthur Rank House provides specialist advice and support for adults with life-limiting illness. The aim of the service is to enable people to live their lives to the full and the focus is on patient choice and quality of life.

People living with life-limiting illness face many uncertainties and have to cope with numerous difficulties. The intention of the service is to look at the person behind the illness, whilst acknowledging the impact that their circumstances have had on them and their loved ones.

Patients attending will have access to a skilled team of professionals who are able to offer help and advice for symptom management, accessing practical help and emotional support.

Physical symptoms can be debilitating and affect quality of life. Symptoms such as pain and nausea can be assessed and monitored by the Specialist Nursing and Medical Team. Physiotherapists and Occupational Therapists run group sessions to enable people to manage symptoms of breathlessness, fatigue and anxiety and people are encouraged to share their experiences with others in similar circumstances.

Complementary Therapists offer relaxation and treatments tailored to individual wishes and needs. Creative activity is also available. The activities range from arts and crafts to music and facilitate motivation and distraction from symptoms. Individually tailored achievable suggestions are derived through discussion. Reminiscence is also hugely significant in enabling conversations and focusing on the person and not just the illness.

Some people benefit from being able to share experiences with others in similar situations and some just find solace in being able to relax peacefully in a safe and therapeutic environment, without feeling the pressure to have to talk.

For some people the opportunity to come to a friendly, welcoming environment can be paramount to their emotional support. Having the time and space in a safe environment to talk about future care and explore difficult questions can be significantly reassuring. There are always people on hand to support these one-to-one conversations: from Chaplaincy to volunteers. The Chaplaincy team are available to all, whether they consider themselves to have a faith or no faith. Volunteers have multiple roles, from catering to providing transport, as well as emotional support. For more complex emotional needs, professional and volunteer Psychotherapists and Counsellors are available. For more practical, social and financial advice, a Social Worker is on hand.

All in all, the aim is that each individual's needs are catered for and quality of life and self-esteem are achieved.

(Louise Rogers, July 2012)

Day Therapy User's Reflections - Bernard

The best bit of Day Therapy was getting out and meeting people, it's better than sitting at home looking at the same four walls and not seeing people. I used to go to Arthur Rank House on a Tuesday – it was just literally getting me out, because if I don't I'm falling asleep and not doing anything. So when I first went to Day Therapy, I was a bit apprehensive but when I met the staff, volunteers and other patients, I found it to be a good experience and enjoyed the session. The lunch was very good and the activities provided kept your mind going rather, as opposed to sitting at home feeling demotivated. I enjoyed it when the children from two local schools visited, and we sat making trees together – it was great therapy. It was good to meet people at the younger end of the spectrum rather than just the older end; they were a great bunch of people when I was there, everybody just mucked in and had some fun.

(Bernard)

Patient Voice: Day Therapy - Maureen

As a volunteer of seven years then a patient, I was very apprehensive but the moment I came through the door I knew I had no need to worry.

Now I feel that I have achieved my goals, I feel more contented and hope that I will have taken some of the pressure from my family later on.

People, including patients, have told me that I have continued in my voluntary work by supporting them through listening and offering some support through their difficult times.

I always think about death but it's about how you can make life so much better. It's wonderful here!

(Maureen)

Creative and Diversional Therapy

The title "Creative and Diversional Activity Co-ordinator" is quite a mouthful. Katie Parker is clear in her description that the aim of her work is to facilitate motivation through creativity, her motto being "process not product".

This approach encourages people, who may be anxious, to try things for fun. "It is also a welcome distraction from any pain or anxiety associated with the patient's condition, as well as helping them practise motor and cognitive skills that may be deteriorating, helping to restore self-esteem".

For Katie, the week is structured; currently patients are offered Day Therapy on three days a week. Each day is patterned but what Katie offers can vary greatly, depending on how many people come in and on their individual needs. "I address the group and ask is there anything I can supply, so that if I do get into a conversation with someone, I am not ignoring other people. If a lot of people immediately want me, I do the quickest request first. I help people create whatever they want or I just sit and listen to them talking. If there's nothing particular required, then I will get out an activity such as weaving and do it in front of people and engage in conversation – it may inspire them to join in or reminisce".

While patients may be engaged in some activity, other members of staff may interrupt in pursuit of other needs a patient may have, so flexibility is essential.

The day is always organised from the patient's need first. Patients themselves have an agenda for that day and they need to achieve it or as much as possible during the time. Their day will include being invited to work in small groups run by the physiotherapist or occupational therapist – teaching as well as sharing experiences about fatigue, breathlessness, anxiety or relaxation. The morning session will end with "Reflections" led by the Chaplain. After lunch, Katie will organise something more relaxing such as reading poetry, a quiz or reminiscence.

She does have a list of activities but the baseline is that patients can think of what they would like to do and Katie aims to respond. She finds that people may like to do some kind of celebration work: such as writing their life story, a book, DVD or memory box. The volunteers who assist her may help by listening to a patient, helping with filming, recording and transcribing. Recently, there have been volunteers who can do book formatting and video editing.

When asked what had been her most challenging requests from patients, the answers all involved messy activities! One time involved the whole group wanting to make hand casts. In order to make such a cast, Katie uses Alginate, a jelly-like material used by dentists in their work! It has to be mixed up and used fairly quickly before it sets. This means going round the room quickly and pouring it onto patients' hands to make the basic mould. After it has set and been removed, the resulting moulds have plaster of paris poured into them from a huge bucket. Inevitably, at least one cast has a tiny hole and so the mix goes onto the floor causing much laughter. The final casts are great, but the clearing up goes on for ages.

Katie's favourite medium is clay. It is good for manipulation, squeezes well and, perhaps most importantly, lots of people have not tried it already so they have no preconceptions about what they can achieve.

The craft room is available to all patients at ARH and sometimes Katie visits people at home so they can try something new in their own time or maybe to offer help with their home computer. Patients and families and especially visiting children can use material from the craft room in IPU.

Brief Biography

Katie first worked at ARH as a volunteer. Then she was employed by Rosetta Life Charity as artist-in-residence doing maternity cover. In 2009, she got her present role which also involves, apart from some time spent in IPU, seeing out-patients, usually on a Wednesday (when there is no Day Therapy) as well as the home visits mentioned.

Patient Voice: A Little Help from Day Therapy - Ann

The encouragement they give us, to partake in things you think you can't do, is very special. I can't draw... then you realise you can give anything a bash! The wonderful team work with us, and the support they give me to try new things. They bring out new things in you, more than one new thing from me!

The hospice is an inspirational place. One or two of us are having rough days today – but we carry each other through it together. The binding memories we have made here will travel with me for the rest of my life. Such special people.

You've given me encouragement, an ear to listen and support. I didn't think somewhere like this existed. It's great to see the children here; to witness it's not a scary place. *(Ann, who suffers from Motor Neurone Disease)*

Complementary Therapy

Complementary therapy is currently organised by Angela Chisholm who established its use at Arthur Rank House. Angela trained as a nurse in Nottingham and specialised in ophthalmics. Having come to Cambridge, Angela trained as a complementary therapist 20 years ago.

Once trained, Angela decided to work at Arthur Rank House and did so as a bank nurse, while running her own complementary therapy practice from her home. After a few months working at ARH, Sheila Walton, the then Principal, gave her permission to do gentle touch treatments on patients, using essential oils. She did this initially as a volunteer alongside her nursing. Later, Sheila Walton asked her to promote complementary therapy at ARH as a paid member of staff. Dr Tim Hunt was very supportive of this initiative and Arthur Rank House was one of the very first hospices to offer complementary therapies to patients and carers.

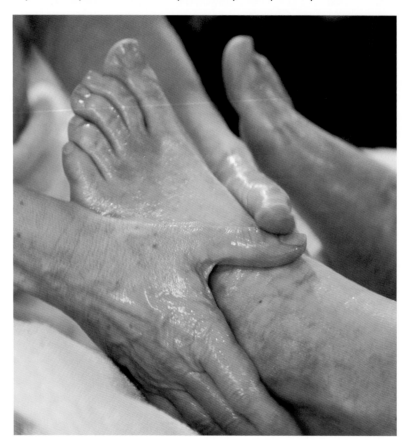

The establishment of the Bernard Reiss Day Centre provided proper facilities for treatment rooms for complementary therapy, as well as the rest of the work carried out in that part of the hospice building. There are now three paid therapists at ARH, with a new post for a complementary therapist to work with Hospice at Home patients and their carers. All patients, carers and the bereaved are offered complementary therapies: aromatherapy, massage alone or with essential oils, reflexology, reiki, H.E.A.R.T.S. (a form of touch over clothing) and relaxation. People are seen in IPU, Day Therapy, in the community and also as out-patients.

"All the therapists are committed to this form of care and feel a deep sense of privilege at the depth and quality of the experiences they are able to share with their patients". All sessions are individual and depend on patients' or carers' needs and diagnoses.

Patient Story

Angela had a carer come to her who had been in agony with neck, shoulder and back pain. She had been to see her GP and had been given lots of analgesics, which hadn't helped. She had been to see a physiotherapist; that hadn't been much help. Now she was waiting to have an MRI scan to see if the cause of the pain could be diagnosed. After two or three sessions with Angela, she came in and said: "You've cured me". Angela said she replied: "No, you've cured yourself, you've relaxed. You had held your muscles so tight – I've just put you on the healing road".

Managing Symptoms without Medicines

The main misconception people have about a hospice, any hospice, has already been referred to and it is that, if you cross the threshold, you are about to die. It is a deep-seated fear and view of what happens in a hospice. Partly it is held because so much of what goes on is neither visible nor talked about. So let's lift the curtain on a very important, hidden, part of the work of Arthur Rank House.

Breathlessness, together with fatigue and anxiety, are some of the most challenging symptoms encountered by patients with cancer, chronic lung disease and neurological or heart disease. Many patients who experience breathlessness find it distressing as it can seriously impact on how they are able to do day-to-day things. Many lose their confidence and feel socially isolated because they are unable to go out with their family and friends or participate in normal family life, leaving them feeling dejected and anxious.

People can attend group sessions as part of Day Therapy or as an out-patient in Ely. Sometimes people are seen at home or as an out-patient for more comprehensive work, or for more complex management techniques, or if they don't feel confident with group sessions. An occupational therapist or physiotherapist facilitates the sessions. During the four sessions, topics such as the causes of breathlessness, links between breathlessness and anxiety and energy levels, as well as how to manage and cope with difficult thoughts and fears are all explored. Treatments and interventions offered include breathing and relaxation exercises, positioning, breathing control techniques, management of anxiety and management of reduced energy.

Patients find these sessions provide them with a welcome opportunity to learn about their breathlessness and other symptoms and understand how it affects their lives and the lives of their families. Using a hand-held fan or learning which positions lessen the sense of breathlessness can reduce symptoms significantly.

Patient Voice: Day Therapy - Anon

I was allocated 12 weeks [of Day Therapy].
I didn't know what to expect; I hadn't heard of anyone who'd been here.

I knew there were therapies but that was it really. I knew it was part of the Hospice and it made me feel the Hospice is where people go to die.

But when I came for assessment, my first impression was about friendliness and cheerfulness and that's good.

No one makes you do anything and I can always do with a bit of laughter.
I really want to enjoy my time and sometimes it gets a bit difficult to enjoy.

My favourite aspect is the therapy massage on my feet and hands. It is relaxing especially as I can't reach my feet.

The most beneficial aspect for me is talking with experts, having time to talk and finding out what's normal.

At the GP surgery, they have no specific experience and I have no idea whether the advice they give is good or bad. Here they understand my illness and the problems associated with it.

My illness is quite unusual but when I went to the breathlessness clinic, everyone had COPD and the symptoms they had were very similar.
I feel I have been sorted.

Did you dislike anything?
No. If I'm being talked to or having something done I enjoy the relaxation in between in the lovely chairs.

Have you any advice for newcomers?
Just go with the flow. (Anon)

Patient Voice: Day Therapy - Anon

....

What did you think when you were first offered a place at Arthur Rank Day Therapy? What did you think?

Not very good.
Ah, scared out of my comfort zone … it was …fear of the unknown.

And what did you know about hospices?

Not very good …

Had you ever experienced Arthur Rank with any of your family?

No.

How did you feel on your first day? How did you get here?

By taxi; it was quite enjoyable, actually …
It surprised me … it was the getting out, and on my own …
It was easy. 'Cause I was away from that comfort zone: and away from "can't do that …" instead of letting me get on and try. My family … I shouldn't say it but it's too good because they're all there … they won't let me, won't let me breathe. But I enjoyed it and the first day was fantastic.

Did you have some goals you wanted to achieve? Do you remember having goals?

Yes, I wanted to … to get out in the garden, 'cause I love my garden. I hadn't been out there for months. But my husband's now put flowers in pots all round the garden, so I can reach them, 'cause I couldn't before. So it's nice to see stuff growing now.

And that's because you got yourself a walker?

Yes.
See, I can't go without oxygen …
Small oxygen bowls don't last to go out and visit and all that.
Yeah, here I am fortunate, I come in here on the little bowl and you switch me to the big, don't ya....
So it's got to be somewhere like that.
That can cope with …
I'm going to see the specialist on Thursday; I'm going to ask him about this conserver that you can put on to it.
Ahh, to sort of compress it … so you don't use very much.
Brilliant. And I learned that off the people here.

So what was your favourite bit about being here?

Mixing with different people. Thinking you're ill, until you come to a place like this. And then you feel alive!!

That's exactly what I like .. for everyone to feel alive ... That's 'cause, 'cause
when you're ...
And when you're like I was ... yes, I was depressed ... then it was a case of ... you
come here and you think I'm bloody lucky I was ... what are you moaning about?
(Anon)

Day Therapy: New Volunteer

After taking early retirement, Denise was steered towards volunteering by
a friend who works at the Hospice and sent her the relevant forms. Having
been accepted and while waiting for her CRB (Criminal Record Bureau)
check, which is needed to work at ARH, she started working at the Regent
Street shop as a volunteer. Denise found she enjoyed this so much, "such
good company", that she has stayed, even after she started in Day Therapy.

Denise's induction to working in Day Therapy was by shadowing three
different people on three occasions. She thinks it's an advantage to shadow
several people, as it gives a sense of how things can be done differently. She is
a volunteer cook. Usually there are two cooks plus two volunteers, one who
may be doing hand massage, while the other talks and listens. Denise was
ready to do her first session as a 'trained' cook just after Christmas and then
found she was doing it solo as her companion cook was ill! "Everyone said, 'if
you need help just tell me'". She did feel a bit nervous as she didn't know the
patients. However, she was reassured by a nurse who said often what people
coming to the Day Centre most needed was to relax and there was room for
every kind of person.

Over the short time she has worked there, she has already found that she
herself is more relaxed and that people do want to talk. Someone may say
things to her that they wouldn't say to family: "I felt like a sounding board and
that has helped me understand the role better".

What is the pattern of your day?

"I arrive at around 10.00am and do a Health and Safety check and wipe the
surfaces. We've all done a food hygiene course. I collect the key (for the
drinks cupboard, so if anyone wants a glass of wine or whatever they can)

and get ready to greet the patients with tea or coffee when they arrive about 10.30. They are brought by taxi, volunteer driver or relative.

There is a 'handover' by medical staff on a 'need-to-know basis'; maybe someone has difficulty in swallowing so 'don't make anything too dry' or 'be aware', someone is having a bad patch. It is absolutely clear that we are not allowed to do anything medical.

We always do a main and a pudding. If someone doesn't feel like eating much, there's always soup or a baked potato. In my head, I'm cooking for a family. There are usually 7–10 people, occasionally fewer, so, as I'm coming to ARH, I'm thinking about what I might cook – maybe stewed plums and custard or rice pudding. Everyone sits round the table after lunch and talks and talks. Patients leave around 3.30, so at 3.00 we offer tea and a slice of cake. Cake features heavily at ARH!" People who come to collect the patients are also offered tea and cake. Denise leaves by 4.00pm normally.

Denise is about to go on a manicure training course with three others so, when that has been completed, they will be able to offer people a manicure when they come to the Centre.

"You do find you get to know patients, remember their names, know what they take in their tea and coffee. Though they only come on a Tuesday, you do build up a relationship. Normally people come for about 12 weeks, but sometimes that is extended by two or three weeks. I do understand a lady who recently said, 'What am I going to do? I'll miss it so'.

People need normality. Day Therapy is the right environment. I personally think it's wonderful and not well enough known".

(Denise McLarnon was interviewed January 2013. She is a retired primary school teacher and combines being a volunteer cook in Day Therapy with helping in the Regent Street shop.)

Patient Voice: Day Therapy - Louise

I have progressed from not being able to drink here and today I've had a cup of tea and half a glass of apple juice, a piece of quiche and ice cream.

It's about encouragement. Everybody is encouraging: nobody patronises. No matter what's wrong with someone you feel relaxed and accepted. Not made to feel the lack of progress/disease is your fault. My doctor made me feel full of blame. (Louise)

Milestones

Milestones – allow us to measure. Milestones are markers which allow time for reflection, review and restatement of goals. Milestones also allow us to hear voices from the past and share their thoughts as they evaluate the work and aspirations of Arthur Rank House from its beginning.

Metaphorical milestones as markers usually occur as people observe a particular passage of time – "our tenth birthday", but they can also come at moments of recognition, perhaps of an individual's contribution to the joint enterprise or a perceived need to change the organisation or its relationship with the wider community.

Milestone: The First 36 Months

In 1984, just before retiring, Dr David Bratherton, first Medical Director of Arthur Rank House, reflected:

The First Thirty-Six Months

"Arthur Rank House opened its doors to the first patient on 14 May, 1981, and this is an opportune time to look back and assess what has been achieved. I remember the great sense of excitement of those early days when 20 years of planning, plotting and pleading finally resulted in a purpose-built building and the promise of the Health Service to meet the cost of running it.

Turning the first sod...Sheila Hancock, Sir Francis Pemberton and others...

The problem throughout those years of waiting had always been one of priorities in the NHS. Great things had been achieved: Addenbrooke's had been raised up from a small provincial hospital to a major centre of innovation and excellence. The new hospital had been built and a new clinical school to train doctors in the latest technology had been created. Many new operations such as hip replacements and coronary artery bypass had restored patients to a fully active life again. The wards were busy and purposeful and yet the feeling had grown that at a certain time in a patient's illness, something more is required: a quieter pace, more personal attention. Nobody felt this more keenly than the nursing staff. As the time a patient spends on a ward has grown less and less, they are not able to get to know them and cope with their problems.

Thus it was that the climate of opinion changed in favour of setting up Arthur Rank House. Half the cost of the building came from the Arthur Rank Foundation through the good offices of the Cancer Relief Society and half was given by the generous people of Cambridge and surrounding villages. I was doubtful that the money would be raised as the million pound appeal for the cancer scanner was running at the same time but I need not have worried. I have memories of Sheila Hancock cutting the first sod in a snowstorm and Lady Todd balancing precariously on the top of a ladder at the topping-out ceremony.

A Case a Day

The number of patients has grown so that now an average of one case a day is referred to the unit. We are very fortunate in Cambridge both in our small city community life and in the excellence of our family doctors but in turn, they appreciate the extra care that Arthur Rank can provide. The medical knowledge is now becoming more widely known. I would never claim we have a monopoly of that but I do feel that we are supremely well placed to look after the families of our patients.

The efforts of the Friends have been invaluable in this respect. The public seems to appreciate what we are trying to do and their generous donations have enabled many extra pieces of nursing equipment to be bought and have paid for staff to go to other training centres to keep up their expertise in modern methods of management of ill patients. We hope, with the assistance of all our helpers, to continue the work that has started so well. We have visitors from other towns asking for advice and we now feel that we can start them on their way and show them how to avoid the pitfalls."

Visit of Prince Charles to Arthur Rank House, November 2002

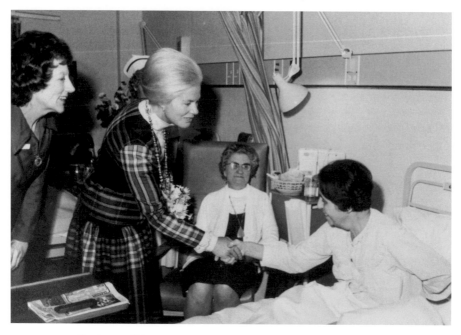

Duchess of Kent opening Arthur Rank House, October 1981

Milestone: 10 Years on

Sometimes, looking back at milestones, and the context in which they were reached, helps us to see how far we have come. The situation in 1991, as described by Dr Tim Hunt below, has changed quite radically. The NHS still contributes funding to the hospice, but it is less that 2/3 of the running costs of the hospice and ancillary services. An example of this change, described in later sections, is that there is now a good support service (Hospice at Home) for patients who wish to die in their own homes and that this service continues to grow.

1991 – 10 years on – Dr Tim Hunt, Consultant Physician Arthur Rank House, reflected on the development of the hospice movement as he saw it then. Part of his assessment follows:

"On the professional front, the term "palliative medicine" is now the approved specialty title for the work that is done in hospices and palliative medicine is now treated much in the same way as anaesthetics or gynaecology. A major step has been taken by the General Medical Council. It has agreed that palliative care will be included as a separate subject in medical training.

Looking at the hospices themselves, there are now over 100 in the British Isles, and they show enormous variety in their size, standards and organisation. Only 12 of these (and ARH is one) are fully funded by the NHS. All other hospices are in the voluntary sector and while they may receive some local health service funds, they rely heavily on voluntary funding. It will not have escaped the thoughts of politicians that if so many units rely and survive on voluntary funding, then maybe the 12 NHS units could, or should, be moved into the voluntary sector, thus freeing money for other health service priorities. Arthur Rank House may have to face this issue one day!

There is now a continual public demand for local hospices throughout the country and while it is relatively easy to tap public goodwill and raise money for hospice buildings, there are big problems in securing funds for their operating costs throughout the year. On average, five new hospices a year are being opened compared to one a year when ARH was opened in 1981.

Do we need so many hospices around the country? Presumably there is good reason for this increase in public demand but, unfortunately, emotion and opinion do not always take account of the fact that the greatest use must be made of limited resources. It may be that future efforts should not be directed towards the building of more hospices but instead towards looking after patients at home. Established hospices could and should then act as centres of excellence in problem solving and education. This would help ensure the continuing high standards that the specialty demands.

Sadly, when we talk about looking after patients at home, our existing health service cannot demonstrate that it has either the money or the strength of organisation to provide proper care and support for the many patients and elderly people who wish to remain at home."

Milestone: Logo - Instant Recognition

"A good logo is eye-catching and provides instant recognition"

The Friends' Logo - 1985

The designer of the logo, Raymond Tomkinson, Senior Nurse, Continuing Care, prepared his design with the following considerations in mind:
"that it should reflect the philosophy of the services on our site, and that it should reflect the locality and history of the site. The tree, in spring foliage and blossom, symbolises hope, new life, and personal growth; it is also reminiscent of the orchard in our midst. The lines beneath the tree represent flowing water, water in turn being a symbol of life. Finally, the tree and the water together form a play on the word 'Brookfields', which is in itself a reminder of the site as a natural choice for health care before 1893".

Charity Registration Number 283353

The Arthur Rank Hospice Charity Logo - 2008

"Our new design reflects the original idea. The tree symbolises hope, new life and personal growth and reminds us of the old orchard on the Brookfields site; several of these apple and pear trees still remain. The flowing lines of the design represent water – again a symbol of life. The combination of the tree and water form a play on the word 'Brookfields' and the incorporation of the letters ARH in the design will, we hope, ensure instant recognition" (Katie Parker designed the new logo).

Arthur Rank
Hospice Charity
A Registered Charity No. 1133354

Making Every Moment Count

The Arthur Rank Hospice Charity Logo - 2012

"Designing a new logo is not a simple task. Accepting an offer of help from Cambridge University Press marketing staff last year, the Charity was told that it needed to develop (and stick to) strong branding guidelines. To follow this advice would mean adopting a new logo. Staff were very concerned and said, 'whatever else happened, the logo had to remain'. Eventually a more flexible approach was agreed, so that as long as the new version was easily recognisable as being 'in the same family', the logo could evolve. We believe that this has been achieved with our newest design".

Lymphoedema Clinic

The Lymphoedema Clinic was set up in the early 1990s by Dr Janet McCabe, the then Senior Medical Officer for Arthur Rank House. It was one of the first clinics in the country to provide treatments for all forms of lymphoedema. The ethos of this clinic is that no matter what form of lymphoedema a patient has, it is a chronic long-term condition, and the patient is supported to understand and to best manage the condition. This enables patients to go on to manage the condition themselves on discharge.

Lymphoedema is a chronic and permanent swelling which can affect any area of the body, most commonly affecting the limbs. It results from poor drainage of the body's lymphatic system and can impact on body image, self-esteem and so cause not only physical but also emotional distress. Currently all lymphoedema patients (apart from mild to moderate post-operative breast cancer patients) are referred to the Arthur Rank House clinic from Addenbrooke's Hospital, GPs and other healthcare specialists.

Causes: Primary – lymphoedema may occur from birth through poorly functioning lymph vessels. Secondary – lymphoedema is generally caused by the curative treatments of cancer which can make one more prone to developing it.

Treatment: Over the past 20 years, this has developed and now consists of skincare, compression bandaging, exercise (which can be more energetic than was previously thought), manual lymphatic drainage, kinesio tape and the use of a compression pump. Later this year, an entirely new treatment will be trialed – laser. This is designed to break down fibrotic tissue which impedes the lymph circulation.

Currently the clinic has around 400 patients and each treatment session takes about an hour. It is not a widely-known part of the Hospice's work and yet has made a major contribution to the lives of many people during the last couple of decades.

Milestone: 20 Years on

Twenty years on, Dr Tim Hunt, Consultant in Palliative Medicine at ARH reflects:

Today, as I look at the activities of the volunteers and the Arthur Rank Hospice Charity, it is difficult to conceive the enormous developments during these 20 years in their work for patients, relatives and staff. The two greatest changes are first in the role of volunteers and second, the increasing financial support from the Charity.

In the early years, some professionals looked aghast at the very suggestion that volunteers should have contact with patients. There were the complex issues of confidentiality, volunteers may broadcast loud and wide details of the patients. What about possible injury or other harm to the patient, or indeed to the volunteer if, for example, an intoxicated volunteer had an accident pushing a wheelchair? Then there was the "union influence" – could this free labour be the thin end of the wedge in usurping the paid professional? When at last a few volunteers were appointed, after a rigorous selection process, they became the ambassadors of the Friends and soon gained the confidence of suspicious professionals.

In the early days, relationships between the Friends and management were not always easy. The Friends did not wish to pry or interfere with the running and policy of the unit; the professionals were equally wary in case there was a take-over bid. Donations trickled into the Friends without serious effort to secure funds and these donations were used to assist patients and staff, examples being grants given towards heating and providing a telephone at home, and staff receiving funding for further training. Some of the grants towards patient transport were considerable. Perhaps the most significant travel grant was paying for a relative in North America to visit a dying patient at ARH.

Slowly, the importance of the Friends in making financial contributions increased, and this culminated when a few of us initiated the Appeal for the Day Centre. This clearly established the potential role of the Charity. Since then, their momentum has been speedy, as they have moved into a professional gear to raise the very considerable sums needed to support so many different activities.

The important and indispensable role of volunteers is now firmly established as their work complements that of many paid professionals. They are in their own way as professional as the rest of us, and the future is heavily dependent on the grace and goodness of our volunteers. The Charity has demonstrated its dynamism and enthusiasm and I feel vindicated when several years ago I said that the Friends were as essential to the future of Arthur Rank House as the local Health Authority.

Patient Voice: Talking to the Press - Jean

On the eve of the 20th anniversary of Arthur Rank House opening, the visit of a reporter from the Cambridge Evening News gave the then Matron an opportunity to comment: "There's a lot of laughter here and happy moments" as she tried to dispel popular misconceptions about a hospice being a place of "doom and gloom". She added: "That's not to ignore the fact that at times it can be very sad but it's not a morbid, dismal place. It's a peaceful and happy environment".

The feeling of safety for those who come as patients to ARH is one appreciated by the then patient, Jean Shaw. Diagnosed with terminal leukaemia, she told the reporter: "I came in here with 12 weeks to live and not expecting to come out. But they turned me around and I have been coming in for a week at a time over the last three years". Though frail and breathing with difficulty, Joan continued: "You come in here and it's a beautiful security blanket. Nothing is too much trouble for them". (16 June 2001)

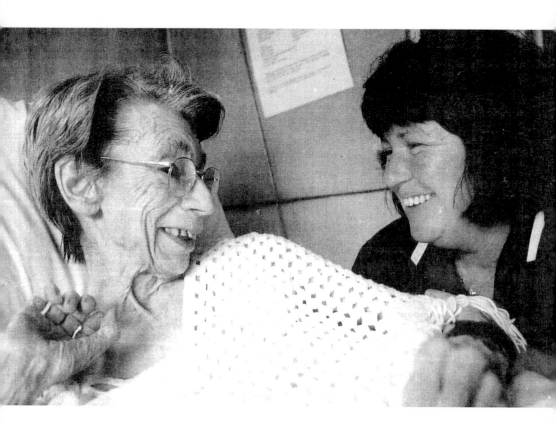

Business Support Manager

"Business Support Manager" – another Arthur Rank House job title that does not immediately reveal what it is that person does! Andrea Long describes her job as being "a bit like a hotel manager". She manages the administrative team, the NHS staff, of Arthur Rank House as well as the facilities. It is the housekeeping. When the loo overflows, a new photocopier is needed, these are issues for her to deal with, as well as having an oversight of finances with Liz Webb (Matron).

It is worthwhile listing the non-medical staff for whom she is responsible, since this list shows the diversity of the work carried out by ARH:

> Receptionist
> Ward Clerk
> Lymphoedema Secretary
> Referrals Officer
> Patient and Family Support Team PA
> Event Co-ordinator
> Chaplaincy PA
> Secretary for Day Therapy
> PA to Matron
> Hospice at Home Secretary
> Voluntary Services Secretary
> Community Nurses Secretary

Andrea is fairly new in post and one of her first impressions of Arthur Rank House was that: "It is lovely, peaceful. Though there is hustle and bustle, it is a calm environment, (even if there is fast paddling below the surface)". Like many people who work at ARH, she finds that people often respond to discovering what her job is by saying, "Oh, I couldn't do that!" though they are often curious as to what the Hospice is like. For Andrea, one of the powerful aspects of her ARH work is that: "Everyone here has a greater value for life when faced with mortality. I won't take so much for granted, I will ignore the inconsequentials, what's on the periphery, and concentrate on what I believe in".

Andrea is clear that Arthur Rank House "provides a lot of choice and a lot of support that are not properly recognised. It is a difficult facility to make shiny. You go into a shop and get good service and so you recommend it. But you aren't necessarily going to go round in the community saying how wonderful ARH is, unless the topic specifically comes up". "It's just a wonderful, wonderful place, doing wonderful things, just a shame we're scared of its connotations".

(Interviewed February 2013)

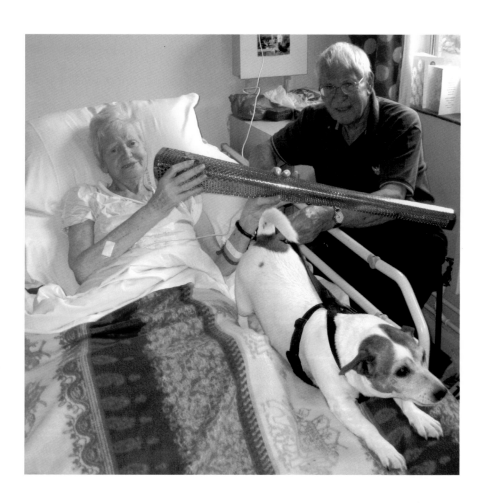

Volunteers: The Dog Lady

For obvious organisational reasons, this story of Arthur Rank House is split up roughly according to function and role, but that, of course, is not what real life is like.

We hope we have showed that the purpose and principles of hospice care are active throughout all of ARH activities and are felt by everyone, whatever aspect of its work or care they come into contact with. The lack of division_ or barrier between IPU and Day Therapy can be seen if one looks at the current work of one volunteer whose story follows. Sarah's interaction with ARH exemplifies the way people find the niche that best suits them and the way they can use their talents to the greatest effect.

This is the story of "The Dog Lady" whose first remark when being interviewed for this book was: "One's really there as a listener".

"One's really there as a listener"

How did it all begin?

My last child started full-time school. I wanted to do something. I heard on the radio the ARH wanted volunteers and I had a good friend who was a volunteer. Rosemary Watson

was the Volunteer Co-ordinator and they ran amazing induction days then. Tim Hunt was excellent – I still remember him saying: "You put on a cloak when you enter this building and you take it off when you leave", as a way of not being burdened by the work. We wore lemon aprons – we were known as "lemon ladies"! We felt like a great little team, those of us who had done the induction together.

I started working in clinics for Tim Hunt
then I helped in the Lymphoedema Clinic
then I helped on the wards
then I helped in Day Care
and that led to becoming "the dog lady"!

I didn't do Day Care for long as we got a retriever puppy, Mimi, and I said I would not be able to come in for a while as I had this young puppy. I was encouraged to bring her in, "everyone would love to see her", and they did. So we trained her as a PAT dog.

Mimi and I then worked together for 10 years. She has recently retired but Bertie – a labradoodle – has taken over from her and proved equally up to the job. Our pattern is to start in Day Care and walk round seeing people and then go to IPU. If things are not busy, it may take half to three-quarters of an hour. The longest we're supposed to do is two hours but it has been three on occasion. It's so lovely, so informal.

The dogs know they're going to "work". Mimi had her own bag, I'd show her the bag and she'd know it was work. Bertie I tell, "We're going to work today". At the end of a session, they get into the car, get great praise and a treat. Bertie came in with Mimi to see what happened and then took over. Now she's quite happy to see him go off, but she does sniff him very seriously when he returns. We usually have a good run – a romp – at the end of a session.

Arthur Rank Hospice is a very special place, people come in in troubled states and feel safe, cared for and understood. They find people who will listen to them. I find it a tremendous privilege [to be at ARH] and [that] at such a critical stage in their lives people let you in – it's rather a wonderful thing.

Often people are really scared when they arrive at ARH whether for the Lymphoedema Clinic, Day Care or as an in-patient. People say to me, "I never thought I'd end up in a hospice", or, "I suppose this is IT". I'm able to say to people: "You'll be offered all sorts of lovely pampering and my advice is to accept it all. The aim is to get you well enough to go home". The second week when I return there has usually been a dramatic change. People often arrive with pain, sickness, depression, no self-worth and wanting to give up. But ARH does not just care for the patient but is so caring of the whole family – you see the most marvellous things. A man who came to IPU said to me, "My one regret is that I want to see one of these gentle giants again" (a Suffolk Punch horse) and ARH arranged for one to be brought to the hospice. Within a week, the man had died but seeing the horse there fulfilled his wishes, his dreams.

I love it [ARH], coming once a week and the difference I see – every whim catered for.

What do the dogs get out of it?

I think they know they're doing something special. They are so calm, gentle, accommodating. The dogs don't act as if there's anything different and yet there are strange, sometimes strong, smells and tubes and so on. I think they pick up they're there for a very special reason. Occasionally people can be a bit rough in their handling of them but they know it's not "play" and they know they're not to put their paws up.

People look at Bertie and say, "What is he?" and I say, "What do you think he is?" and it's an easy way to start a conversation. Or, as I go round the IPU, I can put my head round the door and ask if they would like Bertie and me to come in – it's a relaxed way to begin a conversation. Patients kiss and cuddle the dogs. And I hear every dog story – people think I'm an expert! It takes them out of their illness. Patients will talk to the dog and often are able to say things to Mimi or Bertie that they find too difficult to say directly to another person or they may say, "I'm sad today" or "I'm happy today" to the dog. I've seen tears of sadness and tears of joy.

(Sarah Bradbury was interviewed 11 September 2012. She has been a volunteer for 20 years. Mimi was presented to Prince Charles on his visit to Arthur Rank House in 2002 and was given a special 10-year service award in the summer of 2012).

"This painting was inspired by stained-glass windows and created by 46 people who use Day Therapy or work or volunteer there. Each person chose a section to paint and most followed the general blue/green theme, but, as you can see, there were a few rebels!" *(Katie Parker)*

Milestone: 30 Years on

This book, 'Tears, Love, Laughter' has
been produced to celebrate the
more than 30 years since the founding
of the Arthur Rank Hospice.

Patient and Family Support

From the beginning, Arthur Rank House saw that care and support should surround not just the patient but their family (and friends) as well.

One of the first appointments in 1981 was that of Celia Lindsay as Medical Social Worker. Not only did she have, as Bernard Reiss wrote: "A key role in relating home care with in-patient care and in identifying the needs of patients and their families that could be met by the Friends", but, as he went on to acknowledge: "These needs were sometimes material but always there are emotional needs".

One way Arthur Rank House tried to meet these needs was by setting up "Family Support" with volunteers under the direction and training of Celia Lindsay and Kathy Hines (Home Care Sister). This project had the strong backing of Christine McCrum (Chairman of the Friends) and co-ordinator of the group.

At the same time, the spiritual needs of patients were supported by the Hospice Chaplain, Brother Edgar. He was clear that: "There is something of the human spirit, something in the lives of men and women, committed or not committed to a religious faith, which is evident in these situations".

Supporting those facing terminal illness, whether they have material, emotional or spiritual needs, was a clearly articulated desire and requirement from the first moment of ARH history. Also clearly acknowledged was the need for support for those grieving, facing their bereavement. It is therefore no surprise that if we fast-forward 30 years, the understanding of what is essential in the Hospice's work, what is core to the nature of palliative care, remains the same.

The delivery of this aspect of ARH's work is now carried out, since reorganisation in 2010, by what is called the Psycho-Social Spiritual Team, under Cilla Honniball. However, we shall continue to refer to this area of activity by the more user-friendly title of Patient and Family Support Team, since this is a more direct description of what goes on.

Cilla's Work

In 2010, the existing Psychotherapy and Chaplaincy team were joined by a new (or rather renewed) social worker element. The idea was to have a holistic approach. Cilla herself came from Mental Health and is now linked to Discharge Planning at Addenbrooke's Hospital. Patients coming to ARH for symptom control now have a "timely assessment process for discharge". They are assessed by doctors, nurses, occupational therapists, physiotherapists and social workers. As Cilla says, she is involved with a person's "linear progress through the service provided by ARH". She sees people as having individual pathways. Contrary to so many misconceptions, people "are not here just to die". Lots of people "are absolutely shocked when I start talking about discharge".

Her job involves discussing with a patient what that person needs: benefits, help with housing, practicalities, emotional support, so she can draw on different roles within the Patient and Family Support team to meet those individual needs. She is very clear that: "The person's wishes are respected as far as possible". Cilla can also draw on financial support from the Charity. "As the Social Worker at ARH, I have been able to provide financial support for specific items through the Arthur Rank Hospice Charity's micro grants. Examples of these range from a microwave to enable a lady to have hot meals at home, a new carpet to enable a lady to spend her last months at home in a warm environment, to airline tickets for a family member to enable a young family to be supported through the loss of their mother. Although these grants are relatively small, they have made a huge difference to the end of life for some and the future of others".

Counselling and Bereavement Support

The psychological team currently comprises a psychotherapist, Heather, who is responsible for patients and carer pre-bereavement and a psychotherapist, Leslie, who is responsible for the bereavement service and the volunteers who help run this.

Leslie Davies described how the Bereavement Service "offers emotional and psychological support to the family and friends of patients who were involved with Arthur Rank House at the time of their death. This support is confidential and it may be with our Family Support Team, or with the Psychological Therapist. People may ask why we need specialist bereavement support. The answer is that as society changes, and our rituals around death have changed, bereaved individuals can feel alone and isolated with their grief. Some individuals may need someone to talk to about what is happening to them. Even where there are close family and friends, an individual may want to talk to someone outside of that circle, perhaps if there may be confidential matters that cannot be spoken about easily with loved ones".

In everyone's file is a bereavement form. Family members are asked if they want to be contacted after a patient's death. If they do, then 6–8 weeks after someone has died, contact is made. Leslie sees everyone herself initially. Then most people are seen by a member of the Family Support Team, a trained, dedicated and experienced group of volunteers who offer their time to listen to the bereaved and give them appropriate support. As well as individual support, there is the opportunity for bereaved people to meet and support each other in an informal group setting once a month, in our Bereaved Carers' Group. Leslie describes the aim as enabling people "who are facing life changes through bereavement to find new understanding and new ways of managing those changes".

A Day Therapy patient wrote: "Jonathan the Chaplain told us interesting stories in 'Reflection' and then we listened to music afterwards and it gives you a quiet moment to have a think – it makes you think that life is worth living. The stories Jonathan told were quite inspirational, he would give us more than just two words – it was a good long story. Just before I finished at Day Therapy, I had counselling, to talk about my life and how it's working out. I just hope it does work out better".

Day Therapy User's Reflections - Betty

I felt quite alone when I first came and distant and was reluctant. Once here everything seems so relaxed and feels much better.

Brilliant relationships. People – everyone – not one person I haven't been able to get on with – easy to talk to each other and their problems and you don't feel you're a burden to one person because we're all talking about our problems and they are all different.

I'm not a religious person but I liked talking to Jonathan the Chaplain because he's not like talking to someone in the church. He just made me feel really relaxed. I knew I wasn't going to get religion stuffed down my throat. He respected my feelings about spirituality and didn't judge.

These volunteers do absolute wonders. There hasn't been one meal in 12 weeks I haven't enjoyed.

I speak how I have found everything.

(Betty)

Pre-Bereavement Support

At Arthur Rank House, Heather Styles is the psychotherapist working to offer support to patients, their families and carers at that stage in their lives when they may be finding that living with a life-limiting illness, or supporting someone with such a condition, becomes more than they can cope with. She also works at Addenbrooke's and Papworth hospitals.

Formally, Heather works to support people who are suffering from moderate to severe depression, anxiety and adjustment disorders. Understandably, she finds that the people she sees are wrestling with "existential questions" about the meaning and purpose of life. They may be suffering "a huge amount of fear as well as uncertainty and distress". Facing the end of life "stirs things up from earlier in people's lives ... In my room here, I have seen the rawest distress than anything previously in my working life ... As you can imagine, this is time-limited work – and there are always referrals".

Normally, Heather meets a person (referrals are either the patient or the carer) once or twice to assess them. "We agree what we are going to focus on, and agree the number of sessions we will have. There is already so much uncertainty in their lives it is especially helpful to have this framework". She is aware that hospices vary considerably in respect of the psychological support they offer. On the whole, charity-funded hospices have more or more varied support, but some offer help to the bereaved but do not offer psychological support to patients.

"Death is much further away from people now [than it was in the past]. We are good at denying its existence, denial is a very necessary defence against anxiety, but it also means that what needs to be addressed may not be. If the patient is finding it difficult to speak of dying, I may ask a more open question such as, 'What are your fears for the future?' People's fears are not always about dying but are about relationships. In contemporary British society, death is not seen and so the fear of it has grown. Culturally we live at a time which emphasises youth. There is an innate fear of death, which is proper and right. As a society, we no longer have the same rituals, particularly as we have become so much more secular. However as a nation, we are now more open to the expression of emotion".

Asked what changes she would like to see at Arthur Rank House if she could "wave a magic wand", Heather focused on two areas. Ideally there would be more therapists. In particular, there would be a full-time person and the therapists working at ARH would have different approaches so that there were "two modalities which would enable people to choose which way they wanted to work on their problems". She would also like to see a creative therapist working at the hospice, "so that when someone is stuck for words they can be liberated working in other ways". A final item on her wish list is to have a hospice with a café, where the public come in, "it's about bringing the public in, particularly since we live in an age where we feel we have more control over what happens".

Patient Story

When time is short, communicating well is essential in order to be helpful. The emphasis is on how we resonate and listen to the timbre of each other's being; how we acquire information comes from the feel of our engagement with another person.

Heather asked herself: "How do I meet this person?"
"They're worried about you. Do you mind my talking to you and you talking to me?"

She knew he had been a very physical man and his work with animals had been central to his life alongside his pride in his strength and control. His fear of the ultimate loss of control was showing itself in anger and withdrawal. In response to what he had told her, Heather felt able to say: "You were quite a force to be reckoned with".

In his withdrawal, he had been watching the clock – and waiting. He had actively engaged in speaking, telling her stories and recalling what had been important in his life and what he was proud of. In reviewing his life, albeit briefly, he felt he had regained some control and dignity. They agreed that perhaps a better way for him was literally to turn away from the clock and to actively remember the work and the particular relationship he was proud of.

Bereaved Carers' Group

The group is run by Heather Styles (psychotherapist) and meets monthly. Most people come for 12 sessions. Members spoke of their grief, and of the support that they gained from talking to each other in this group:

Caring and the necessity of caring had gone – it left a huge void

My world was falling apart, and my body too

All my life I've been caring and now I'm not needed any more

Without the volunteer drivers I couldn't get here to these meetings

I wouldn't survive without Arthur Rank

You find connections within the group

Someone's experiencing the same things

Listening and having things given back to me

(Talking about the Bereavement Choir which formed to sing at "Light up a Life", December 2012): I couldn't wait to get here to do that, it was the highlight of my year. I've never sung before – my grandchildren think I've improved (May 2013)

Patient Voice - John

....

Day Therapy has opened up my eyes and I've
thoroughly enjoyed myself. It's been a pleasure to meet
staff and patients.
I've made some friends here.
You are an amazing team.
When compiled you make up a good team - you make
up kindness.
You have got time.
Time is 2nd most important thing bestowed upon us.

I want this at my Funeral:

You come into this world alone.
You depart alone.
The period in between called time, is meant to be shared
with those you love, family and friends.
Thank you for spending your time with me.

The verbal word is soon forgotten: the written word can
be referred to time and time again
Life is the 1st most important thing.

Time – use every single second available to you to
achieve the best you can to make life pleasurable for
yourself and others.
All staff do.
I especially give lots of praise to Jonathan, he's a true
friend what he's said and done has had a good effect on me.
I really enjoyed Reflections I went to every one of the
Reflections. It's changed my point of view.
You can't beat it.
You only get one shot at life. It's not a dress rehearsal.
Extract every single moment.
If you can help someone give pleasure then that's even
more beneficial.
Laughter is the best medicine.

I'm feeling really positive and happy about things and
That's what I want to tell others.

Laugh out my guts.
Tread on my tumor, squash and chuck it in a volcano.
Not going to rise out of the ground like a mummy's grave
Being on the steroids I feel now like before I had chemo.
If I had a magic want I would make everyone feel like me.
I'm thoroughly enjoying how I am, especially with the weather.
(John)

Title: Peasants Dancing

"This watercolour, 'Peasants Dancing', was painted 17–19 June 1987 by Lore Burgess (originally an artist). At that time, Lore was a patient at Arthur Rank House. She was right-handed, but an operation to remove a brain tumour had left her right side paralysed. Occupational therapy with Valerie Bennett at ARH encouraged Lore to start painting again, but using her left hand. We are grateful to be able to use this delightful illustration of one of her last paintings".

Patient and Family Support:
Spirituality - The Chaplaincy

"Spirituality is central to the 'essence of care' and lies at the heart of 'who we are' – both as individuals and an organisation at Arthur Rank House. Spiritual care is provided by all staff, carers, families and other patients – as well as the Chaplain, who is regarded as the 'specialist' and expected to be a member of the multi-disciplinary team". Rev. Jonathan Burrough, the outgoing Chaplain, defined the Chaplain's role and responsibilities as "endeavouring how best to assist in the spiritual and holistic care of all concerned, to understand the whole person, their total pain, physical, psychological, spiritual and social".

"Over the years an excellent team of Chaplaincy volunteers has been trained and appointed. The Chaplaincy are facilitators. There is no proselytising or evangelising and assumptions are not made as to which faith a patient or visitor may or may not practise. We are available to all patients and their families, as well as staff – people of faith or no faith at all – building relationship and trust, willing to explore questions and fears, as well as sometimes simply 'be alongside' people in times of great need".

"There is a difference between 'spiritual' and 'religious'. Spiritual care is usually given in a one-to-one relationship, whereas religious care is about shared beliefs, values, liturgies and lifestyle of a faith community. Some people do put their spirituality in a religious framework, but for other it is less defined, though no less important – relating to the basic question, 'Who am I ?' and 'What makes me who I am?' Everything that happens to and around me impacts upon me and may affect how I am coping. So, when a person is treated with respect, listened to in a meaningful way, seen and treated as a whole person within the context of their life, values and beliefs, then they are receiving 'spiritual care'".

The new Chaplain, Rev. Keith Morrison, arrived at Arthur Rank House early in 2013. He explained his view of the role of Chaplain in a similar way. He sees the role as "being here to help people make some sense of what's going on, to consider their world view and how their situation fits in with it. The role is like that of a 'translator', encompassing both the religious and the spiritual: all those parts of ourselves about who I am, why I am here, what happens next?"

Light up a Life

Every year in November, the Hospice hold its "Light up a Life" memorial service. The service is for anyone who has lost someone, it does not have to be someone who has died in the hospice. The Chaplain takes those present through a chance to think and reflect about lost loved ones. The theme is always spiritual rather than religious. The service is held in the grounds of the Hospice, hundreds of twinkling lights are strung between the trees and the Ely City Military Band add their special magic to the event. Commemorative booklets are produced each year as keepsakes for the participants.

Paradoxically, "Light up a Life" started as a fundraising exercise. It has now become, for those attending, a significant moment through their journey of grief. The atmosphere can be almost overpowering. For some, it is their first time at the ceremony, others have been coming for many years. For all, the seasonal remembrance service is felt to be both a moving and uplifting occasion.

Milestone: Friends of Arthur Rank House

With hindsight, "milestone" can be seen as the correct word to use to reflect the significance of the setting up of the Friends of Arthur Rank House which took place simultaneously with preparations to open the hospice in 1981.

Christine McCrum described how the Friends were formed by David Bratherton, the first Medical Director of Arthur Rank House, and his wife, Mary, with Tim Hunt, the then Senior Clinician. Their aims as formally expressed in the constitution were:

- to supplement the services of the Health Service in relieving patients and former patients, whether resident in the unit or in the community;

- to educate, by encouraging the interest and support of the public in the work of the unit;

- to promote research and the exchange of advice and information by holding conferences, lectures and discussions;

- to raise funds and to provide amenities to relieve patients in need of assistance.

In practical terms, this meant forming a group of volunteers to put these aims into effect.

The committee was formally named "Friends of Arthur Rank House and Brookfields Hospital" (Brookfields being that part of the site which undertook care of the elderly). Christine McCrum became its first Chairman. In due course, the Friends focused only on Arthur Rank House. Significantly, they also moved from being mere receivers of donations to being major fundraisers – for example, their work in generating the major funds needed to build the Day Centre.

As their dedicated work in supporting ARH and supplementing services provided by the NHS grew, it became appropriate formally to turn the Friends into a charity. "The word 'Friends' does not convey the image of an increasingly professional charity which must raise in excess of £400,000 per annum just to sustain existing commitments". And so, in 2000, the Friends duly became "Arthur Rank Hospice Charity". Subsequently, in 2010, the

Charity became a charitable company limited by guarantee which currently raises in excess of £1.2 million to support the work of the Hospice. The following pages explore and reflect both the early days and the current life of the Charity.

Arthur Rank House is licensed for weddings for patients

Arthur Rank Hospice Charity

In seeking to write about what goes on now, it is very clear there are no neat divisions between the Hospice and the Charity, between paid staff and volunteers; though everyone's role is clear and distinct.

There is a considerable and powerful inter-relatedness between Arthur Rank House and the Charity. At a rather simplistic level, it can be seen in the physical layout of the building. Both the Hospice patient activities and the work of the Charity are carried out in the same building. There is a different entrance for the Day Centre from the main reception but everyone else comes through that door (to the warm and sensitive welcome of Shelagh, the Receptionist).

The medical Staff Room is to be found at the end of the corridor past Finance and Fundraising. The first room on the right is the base for the In-Patient Unit Manager, together with Hospice at Home (note that one is funded by the NHS and the other by the Charity.) The next room is that of the Chief Executive of the Charity who shares the space with the Volunteer Manager and her assistant.

Apart from the clear fact of there simply not being enough space in the current building for everyone to work comfortably, this geographical pattern well reflects the interdependence of ARH and the Charity. Currently, the NHS funds two-thirds of the work of Arthur Rank House and one-third is funded by the Arthur Rank Hospice Charity.

In 2001, Dr Tim Hunt, reflecting on 20 years since the Hospice opened, commented: "The two greatest changes are first in the role of volunteers and second, the increasing financial support of the Charity". More than a decade later, the situation is even more keenly felt and it is perhaps appropriate here to say that no national charities currently support any care at ARH.

Arthur Rank Hospice Charity: Interview with the Chief Executive

....

What are people's reaction to your job?

"They frequently say, "You must be very brave" or "You must have a very sad job". But my answer is that the job is always full of emotion, but that one's as likely to hear laughter as tears. It is a privilege – it allows you to see almost instant benefit.

The Charity can make micro grants as a very rapid response to a patient in need. These grants, of £100–200, can be administered within an hour and can make a real difference: such as allowing the surviving parent to buy new clothes for the children to wear to the funeral. If the Matron Liz is short-staffed, the Charity can respond immediately to a request to get agency staff. This feels to be the complete opposite of the NHS – a giant bureaucracy – but the Charity really does make a difference while always working within appropriate and rigorous practices.

Being co-located within the hospice is really important. It allows us to feel part of the hospice and so we all feel a real passion for the job, though we would still feel committed were we differently located. Also being embedded in ARH sometimes lets us see a need and then we may be able to generate suggestions".

What is currently funded by the Charity?

"Apart from Day Therapy and Hospice at Home, the Charity funds patient consumables such as extra food, alcohol and toiletries, and stocks the patients' kitchen so relatives can cook a meal for themselves. It also funds posts: half the Chaplain; Heather, the ward assistant; Katie Parker who runs creative therapy; complementary therapists; support for schools; transport service and support of around 300 volunteers, who are managed by Anna Croft and her assistant, Gina, refurbishment projects such as new floor, curtains, furniture etc. in the Day Therapy room, plants for the garden, supplies for the Tea Bar – and I could go on. Daily there are requests: yesterday the In-patient Manager asked for funds to pay for the maintenance of flat screen TVs".

Lynn then described how, because the quality of care the Hospice gives to patients and their families is so excellent, families and friends go on to provide enormous support to Arthur Rank House by helping the Charity raise funds. Thus the funding of care is like a virtuous circle and the Hospice is embedded in the community.

"It is important to point to the future to the 'continuum of the journey'. We do need to think about the next 30 years. The bricks and mortar 'are not fit for purpose'. We can do it so much better and we will".
(Lynn Morgan was interviewed August 2012)

Postscript: Personal Story

Lynn's father was in intensive care in Addenbrooke's Hospital and was then transferred to a ward there. He was very poorly indeed. When he arrived at ARH, he couldn't sit up, wasn't eating a yoghurt a day even. First off he was given a jacuzzi bath, made comfortable, and he started to eat. After spending 2–3 weeks at ARH, he walked out of the building to go home. He had another three years of life. He was given TIME and NURTURE. While at ARH, her father had both hand and foot massages – he said it felt as if he were in heaven! *(Interviewed September 2012)*

Suffolk Punch

Every hospice will have its fund of special stories. One we heard featured the visit, by arrangement, of a baby elephant to greet one of the patients.

For us, one of our recent stories also concerns a pre-arranged visit – that of a Suffolk Punch horse.

January of 2012, Richard Gowing was an in-patient at Arthur Rank House. Richard had been President of the Farriery, Blacksmith and Agricultural Engineers Association. He was also a nationally respected judge of Heavy Horses, such as the Suffolk Punch, and had a long association with the Suffolk County Show where he had been a judge for over 30 years. Richard had been due to be honoured for his commitment with a special award and twice this was to have been presented to him by Princess Anne. He had been too ill for this to happen. So the Hospice Charity arranged for a presentation at Arthur Rank House. Richard received his award from the Director of the Suffolk Show and the Suffolk Punch horse in its full splendour also attended the ceremony.

Fundraising

Fundraising as undertaken by the Arthur Rank Hospice Charity can be looked at as being divided between one-off projects and initiatives, and the on-going work to fund the annual responsibilities and contributions of the Charity to the work of Arthur Rank House.

Such divisions are not always tidy in real life. An example of the "one-off" project, already described in some detail, was the fundraising carried out between 1993 and 1995 to raise the funds to build the Day Centre. The Friends of ARH put an enormous amount of work, with others, into providing the building, and the NHS was to provide the running costs. However, difficulties with the latter soon arose.

The Chair of the Friends wrote in 1998: "In the last two issues of the Newsletter I wrote at some length about long-term funding of Day Care and how Friends in close collaboration with Lifespan Healthcare intended to address the problem. I make no apologies for returning to this subject since it continues to occupy our thoughts and much of our time. ... Meanwhile, in the short term, the Friends Committee have agreed to take responsibility for a major part of the funding of Day Care from current resources from 1st April 1998 to bridge the gap". Perhaps it should not be a surprise that the Charity currently, and for some time, has funded the running of Day Therapy in its entirety.

As an example of a contemporary one-off initiative, we can highlight the current work of Robert Barnes' Lisa Barnes Memorial Fund, where his aim is to raise £100,000 in memory of his wife, Lisa, who died in ARH in 2010. This is an extraordinary goal. His ambition and commitment have already resulted in his having raised £72,500 for the Hospice Charity at the time of writing. Such a decision is both humbling and inspirational to everyone working on fundraising as well as those more widely associated with ARH. It does perfectly illustrate what Lynn Morgan, the Charity's Chief Executive, has called the "virtuous circle" of those whose families have benefited from ARH wanting to improve it for those to come.

Looking at the staff of the Charity, it is clear that, with the significant exception of the Volunteer Manager, part-time assistant and transport co-ordinator, everyone else, under the aegis of the Chief Executive, is involved directly in fundraising and finance. The Charity posts, as opposed to the

Robert Barnes fundraiser for Lisa Barnes Memorial Fund – they start young

Hospice posts funded by the Charity, are listed below:

Chief Executive, Fundraising & Marketing Manager, Marketing & Events Officer, Community Fundraisers, Fundraising Administrator, Finance Officer, Finance Assistant, Volunteer Manager, Assistant to Volunteer Manager, Transport Co-ordinator, Senior Shop Manager, Shop Manager and Assistant Shop Manager.

These 13 posts are equivalent to nine full-time posts.

The Arthur Rank Hospice Charity's main sources of income are: Your Hospice Lottery, the Charity's shops, donations, including those given in someone's memory, event participation, regular giving, trusts, community fundraising, corporate support, and wills and legacies. Whatever category support comes from, it is the result of dedicated, hard work by the Charity staff, together with many volunteers within ARH and the Charity as well as the commitment and generosity of the wider community.

Fundraising as part of the on-going work of Charity staff (and volunteers) can be viewed by looking at the annual calendar of charity-organised events together with those initiatives supported by the Charity but taken up by the community.

Annual Calendar of Events

Mar/Apr   Afternoon Tea

May   Star Shine Stroll — a memory night walk

June   Big Bike Ride with Press Relief, the Cambridge News Community
           Fund (shared with other cancer charities — in 2012 with East
           Anglian Children's Hospices, in 2013 the Teenager Cancer Trust)

Sept   Bridge the Gap with Press Relief, the Cambridge News
           Community Fund

Nov   Ely Festive 5K Fun Run

Dec   Light up a Life

Community Initiatives

2012   The Big Quiz

2012   Gold Challenge

2012   Accumulator Challenge

2012/13   Wacky Races (corporate rafting race)

The sources of income for the Charity are very varied but each represents commitment and hard work on the part of donors and reflects the esteem in which Arthur Rank House is held as well as confidence in the Charity.

Peaks and Troughs of Fundraising

Asked to provide personal examples of "Peaks and Troughs", members of staff came up with lots of peaks and practically no troughs!

There is nothing more satisfying than reading the words of a family who have benefited from the care provided by staff at the Hospice. *(LH)*

You have never heard it all when it comes to fundraising. From people like Robert Barnes who set themselves a target to fundraise £100,000 to a local group holding an annual ploughing competition on our behalf, the methods by which people support the Charity are diverse. *(DT)*

Occasionally, things don't always go according to plan. We organised an event in the post-Christmas get-fit season based on a "get muddy and challenge yourself" fun run. "True Grit" was born, but came with a number of challenges of its own. The snow came, the mud froze and the first venue was unusable. A second date was booked but that meant lower numbers, and that meant we were not able to raise as much as we originally set out to achieve. *(TA)*

Mention to a corporate partner the ways in which they and their colleagues can help the Charity, and suddenly you are overwhelmed by the creativity, the energy and the enthusiasm you see before you. *(DT)*

From cake sales to sky dives and quizzes to fire walks, you name it, we've done it! *(AH)*

The beauty of the Hospice is often in the details, entering the ward to see someone's pet curled up at the bottom of the bed, or to see a family enjoying a glass of wine together. *(TA)*

(Contributions from Lynne Hays, Donna Talbot, Tasha Auburn and Aisha Hunt)

Fundraising: A Personal View

Fundraising £1.2 million from the local community as part of a relatively small team is not for the fainthearted! For me, however, it was an extremely rewarding, heartwarming experience which will be looked back on fondly forever.

It didn't take me long to realise that what I had actually signed up to was an "access all areas" pass into an Aladdin's Cave of the most amazing people – from staff, to volunteers, to patients and their relatives, to the many kind-hearted and crazy people living and working within the community – I say crazy because when you understand the lengths some people will go to, to support the Hospice and its Charity. Take for example the group of lads who cycled from Vancouver to Tijuana on nothing but a wing and a prayer!

I was always touched by those who wanted, in their words, "to do something to acknowledge the fantastic work of the Hospice". Take a minute to consider the lengths the Charity's marathon runners go to: not only do many of them hold down a job, support a household, and train to run 26 miles – they then find the time to raise substantial amounts of money for the Hospice. This applies to all those who hold tea parties, golf days and concerts – the list goes on. It is not only the money they give, but the time they give, which means so much.

Working as a fundraiser for the Hospice is a privileged position to be in; often being trusted with relatives' and friends' most treasured memories, and to help celebrate and honour the life of that special someone.

People would often apologise that it is "not much", when handing over money that has been hard-earned, but we always remind them that it is the many little drops that really fill the bucket, and that without them the Hospice would not be what it is today.

The Charity is also lucky enough to be supported by local business, and awarded grants as a result of Trust applications, and there is nothing I enjoyed more than to invite such donors into the Hospice to show them firsthand what they were helping to achieve. Hearing people say on their first visit: "I didn't realise how much goes on here", was important. It was satisfying seeing them relax as they walked around, look admiringly when they understood the vital role of the volunteers – both in terms of the physical care of the patients and of fundraising, and smiling when they saw what a positive, empowering place it can be. The true measure of the place is when at the end of a visit,

I would be asked what volunteering jobs were available, or what more they could do to help. These reactions show what an amazing oasis the Hospice is.

There is also the important job of educating the community about the work of the Hospice, and demonstrating through some of the most wonderful stories that have been shared, that it is not a place to be feared. I think that this belief is what lies behind the strength in the Charity – all passionately working to ensure that it remains well supported so patients and their loved ones are too.

I have only touched on some of the things the Charity does, so I think you can understand what I meant in my opening sentences.

(Lucy Day, Senior Fundraiser, 2012)

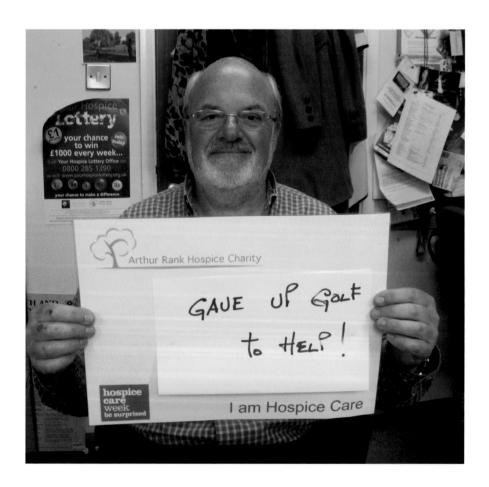

Arthur Rank Hospice Charity: Chair of Trustees

My wife, Brenda, had been a volunteer for several years and I had always been struck by how much she enjoyed the people – patients, volunteers, staff – she worked with. So when I had the opportunity to become a Trustee in June 2007, it took only a few moments to say "yes". I then became Chair of Trustees in December 2008 because I felt there was a big opportunity for the Charity to do even more. So I took the lead in recruiting Lynn Morgan as our first full-time Chief Executive to make sure we could drive forward our new strategic vision.

As this book goes to print, we are working closely with our NHS colleagues to become an independent Hospice. The existing Hospice building in Mill Road, Cambridge, is full of wonderful staff who provide fantastic care. But it no longer provides the physical facilities and services that patients require, expect and deserve. So we are planning to build a new Hospice in or around Cambridge. We will also continue to expand our Hospice at Home services. We have built our financial resources to over £5 million to provide a strong foundation from which to implement our new vision.

Who knows what the next Arthur Rank Hospice Celebration Book will say in 20 or 30 years? But I hope it will continue to demonstrate that the Hospice has always provided care and compassion to patients and their families in our community; and that our services and facilities have remained up-to-date and among the very best in the country.

(Stuart Evans, April 2013)

Brief Biography

Stuart Evans is a Cambridge-based entrepreneur, having been founding Chief Executive Officer at Plastic Logic and Cotag International. He was also a Board Member at the East of England Development Agency and now follows a portfolio career. A graduate of Jesus College, Cambridge and Harvard Business School, Stuart and his wife have lived in Newnham since 1984. They have three adopted children all now adult and still living in Cambridge.

Fundraising: Administrator's View

I have had the pleasure of working with wonderful volunteers over the last 14 years and they have been an enormous help to me personally but none more so than when the Fundraising department used to organise the newsletter mailing in-house. This involved between 16 and 20 volunteers and a frantic morning of stuffing 7,000 addressed envelopes with the newsletter and various flyers. Staff and volunteers, although taking the job in hand seriously, had such a lovely morning of laughter, coffee and sharing stories, that we became friends. I think we shared things we probably wouldn't have shared with anybody else. There was such a lot of banter flying around on those mornings and the morning flew by. One volunteer in particular, who I think would prefer not to be named, used to take as much responsibility as me for getting the mailing out on time. I hope they all realise how much they were appreciated. A large number of the volunteers were with us for eight years, meeting five times a year, and it was such a very sad day when it was no longer viable to continue the mailing in-house. All good things come to an end. We are eternally grateful to all those incredibly reliable volunteers and I think we all miss the drama of whether the job would be finished in time for the Royal Mail van calling to pick it up!

Volunteers who have worked in the Fundraising department are extremely committed and stay for a long time. One of our cash counters has been with us for 10 years, which highlights this commitment. Most seem to stay until they either moved away or really can't get here any longer! Collecting tins being taken out into businesses, inputting data onto our database, seeking venues to place our Christmas and Easter toys, counting money and helping with events are just a few of the ways in which our volunteers have helped us and continue to do so.

In the same way, whoever comes to work here doesn't want to leave: "this is where my heart is" has been heard. It is totally different to any other hospital environment.

(Maureen Thompson, interviewed 14 February 2013 and 2 March 2013)

Going that extra mile – Great Wall of China!

'Girls' on getting a wiggle on – Starshine Stroll: 10 mile walk!

Mexico to Tijuana – no boundaries to their efforts!

Getting stuck into the challenge – True Grit

Hospice at Home: Fulfilling a Last Wish

Neil wanted to share his family's experience of Hospice at Home and what it meant to him, his late wife Jan and the family.

"From the shock of the terminal diagnosis, to Jan's death two years later, we felt we had a friend, and expert, giving us comfort, reassurance and guidance. Our relationship started when Jan's GP referred her to the Hospice at Home nurse, Lorraine Moth. Lorraine understood how important it was to Jan to spend the last days of her life at home.

We were at home together for most of those two years, but Jan's last two months saw several periods in hospital, coinciding with heavy snow, and wards closed due to virus infection. Visiting was severely restricted and Jan was desperate to get home to be able to see family and friends as and when they could reach us. Lorraine could see that precious time was being lost, so she worked hard to make sure Jan could return to her home as soon as possible.

I had always thought, "death happens in hospitals – how could we possibly get the support Jan needs any other way?" However, I soon learnt that this was not the case. The Hospice at Home team ensured everything was in place, which gave Jan the end that she wanted – in control, at peace and surrounded by friends and family. We were strengthened by knowing that the team were always available to give any support and advice needed". *(Neil)*

Hospice at Home: Funding Threatened

Hospice at Home was set up in 1993 after a successful pilot project. As the headline in the local paper shows, this vital service was under threat in 2006 when local NHS money together with support from Marie Curie Cancer Care were withdrawn. The Arthur Rank Hospice Charity had already been helping fund Hospice at Home and the Charity Trustees stepped in with additional funding to keep this service going.

The Charity has fully funded Hospice at Home ever since. Very recently, the new Clinical Commission Group has agreed to put in some funds so that this excellent service can be extended to the rest of Cambridgeshire.

www.cambridge-news.co.uk/news   EVENING NEWS, SATURDAY, JULY 1, 2006

Trustees to rescue of 'hospice at home'

Charity's shock at NHS cuts

■ REBECCA ATTWOOD

MORE cash is being ploughed into a valued "hospice at home" service put at risk by health cuts.

This week, the *News* revealed sweeping cuts to the local NHS service, which included slashing the Arthur Rank Hospice's budget by £400,000 and cuts to its hospice at home service, based at the hospice in Mill Road, Cambridge.

But trustees of the Arthur Rank Hospice Charity have now agreed to inject a further £40,000 into the hospice at home service for the current financial year, in an attempt to safeguard this vital service for cancer patients.

The cash is in addition to the £90,000 the charity already contributes each year to hospice at home.

They have also agreed to take over responsibility for funding of the bereavement counselling services at an annual cost of about £30,000.

Dave Murphy, trustees' chairman, said: "We were naturally devastated by the recent PCT announcement concerning their proposed withdrawal of funding from the hospice at home service.

"For the past two years, we have worked in partnership with the South Cambridgeshire and Cambridge City Primary Care Trusts (PCTs) and Marie Curie Cancer Care to jointly fund this critical service. In order to save it, the charity has acted swiftly to inject these further funds, as we are concerned at the level of anxiety this news will have caused patients and their families."

He said the PCTs had also proposed withdrawing funding from the bereavement counselling service provided at Arthur Rank House.

Mr Murphy said: "We will be stepping in to fund this service if the PCTs' proposed funding cuts are approved in the public consultation process.

"The patients and families relying on hospice at home and bereavement counselling services are at one of the most vulnerable times in their lives. As a charity we cannot stand idly by and let these vital services be withdrawn.

"We will be seeking urgent further meetings with the trusts and Marie Curie to find a long-term way of securing these services.

"We already receive incredible support from our local community, but if it falls to our charity to keep these much-needed services going we will need to increase our fundraising massively. At present we need to raise £700,000 each year and it's obvious this figure is set to increase dramatically."

To make a donation to the hospice, call (01223) 723115.

rebeccaattwood @cambridge-news.co.uk

VITAL SERVICE: Dave Murphy said he was devastated by news of the health budget cuts. Left, Arthur Rank Hospice. Inset: How the *News* reported the cuts.

Cambridge Evening News — TAKING A SCALPEL TO YOUR NHS

Hospice at Home: The Service

What Hospice at Home Does

- It enables more patients to die at home, if they wish;
- It improves the experience of dying;
- It provides personal and emotional care for the patient;
- It provides specialist nursing care;
- It provides support for relatives;
- It provides information;
- It provides bereavement support.

Apart from location, the work of Hospice at Home is, of course, following the same aims and practices as those underpinning the work at Arthur Rank House.

The following qualities are needed to make a good Hospice at Home member of staff:

- Palliative care experience;
- Enthusiasm for the job – "because it can be quite tough sometimes";
- Good communication skills;
- Willingness to work autonomously;
- Ability to work with patients in their own homes and not try to tell them what to do, but to provide support as and when required – and not to provide services that are not wanted.

Hospice at Home: Nurses' Views

These reflections, views, presented here come from the Hospice at Home nurses and care assistants who were interviewed autumn of 2011 as part of a Service Evaluation prepared for Hospice at Home and the Arthur Rank Hospice Charity. Though some comments very clearly come from the reality of working in a person's home, many could just as easily have been made by the staff nursing on the In-Patient Unit at Arthur Rank House itself.

"I'm just really happy working, we get lovely feedback ... and although it doesn't appear on the surface to be a very nice job to do, it's actually really rewarding .... you get that all the time, 'Oh I don't know how you do your job', but we meet such smashing people and it does feel like you make a difference".

"In the quietness of the night, the time when people will grab an hour or two to really explore in a safe way".

"So many people are very fearful of what's going to happen next, and we all want to know in any situation, 'Well what happens next, how long will it be before this?' and there's so many stages that you can start to worry about long before it comes and a lot of people ... who like to be in control ... cope with things much better if (they) know what to expect and I think it takes the fear out of it".

"And there's also psychological support to a patient and relatives. In the middle of the night it's surprising what you learn from patients, they tell you a lot of stuff they don't tell anybody else".

"Families, they're obviously terribly emotional which is so tiring and they're so tired and no-one wants to take a break, people feel very guilty about not being there all the time, and again if you can help them understand that none of those things are really that useful, and they need to sort of hold back a little bit and also enjoy the patient instead of worrying about doing the tiring things, or the patient knowing to save their energy for enjoyable moments with their family".

"Giving relatives a night's sleep which is massive, that's probably more massive than anything".

"What I've kind of found is the patient might say, 'I want to be at home,' but the relatives ... actually take on the brunt of it really because it is quite a lot to have to ask of people, and I think it just makes it achievable. If you're there, you just give [families] that reassurance [which they seek], you help the relatives, just

helpingholding a hand really, just help the relatives through and then they feel that they can manage.....And the patient is getting what they want, really, to be at home ... and in an environment that they feel they've wanted to die in".

"Also explaining who to contact, what to do, not sit there in pain, adapting people to where they're at in their illness".

"I do quite a lot of visualisations with people ... reading to people as well, the lady the other night actually I read to her and she said she'd never been read to since she was a child and she was really excited ... sometimes it can be really bizarre things like I've peeled carrots in the middle of the night before with people ... the carrots needed peeling and you have a big conversation when you're peeling carrots or you're doing something else and people can't sleep a lot of the time".

Decision Making about Preferred Place of Death

The work of Hospice at Home is critical in many ways. One of the obvious being that it enables people to choose to die at home which is what the majority say they would choose. This aspect of Arthur Rank House's work is likely to be increasingly highlighted as the government actively encourages patient choice over preferred place of death.

This is not always a straightforward decision. Listen to the Hospice at Home nurses:

"You know, it's that sort of feeling they have, I can understand that too and I understand it for people with young children, it can go either way can't it? You either have that lovely memory that they are at home and the children are with them and they see them die and it's so natural or you've got this feeling that that room is where mum died so it depends on the other half of the partner really and the carer support they have and it's very interesting. And what experiences they've had in the past".

Patients change their minds about where they would like to die, sometimes more than once. Some patients "are looked after at home and then when they get even more poorly they say, 'that's it, I don't want to be at home', so they come in, so we work in conjunction with the In-Patient Unit which is really good".

Patients sometimes do not choose to die at home, but to be cared for at home. "We have what's called a 'preferred priority of care', which we often ask them, like, you know, 'Where do you want to be when you actually do pass away?' and for the majority of our patients, it is home, but for some of them, it is the In-Patient Unit. But they need us up until a certain point and then they come into the In-Patient Unit for the last two or three days. ... Like, we had one lady recently that .... I think she only had like one night in here and then she passed away, but we were supporting her at home for a good three weeks, I think it was, in the run up to that, so she was able to stay at home for as long as she possibly could"

Hospice at Home: Family Voices

"Kate's wish was to spend the last days of her life at home. The Hospice at Home nurses imbued confidence in any ability we had to cope and they instilled a sense of security and inner peace in their patient, Kate. Their guidance, we believe, allowed Kate to leave as she wished, privately, at peace in her own home, knowing she was very much loved and would be very much missed. Not alone, but surrounded by the love and affection of those that cared for her".

"You enabled her to die with grace and dignity surrounded by people who 'really' care".

"Their unobtrusive presence and help at Bill's last moments, saved us any panicky moments of 'what to do next'".

"Geoff to die at home, surrounded by his familiar things, the sun shining on him through the open patio door, his water feature flowing and us lying on the bed next to him. Thank you Hospice at Home".

"Your organisation did not only help Ken fulfil his wish to die at home, but also helped myself to have some respite during the night. The nurse who cared for my husband was kind, professional, supporting and more importantly caring. I would be grateful if you could relay my sincere gratitude to your team for making a sad experience a peaceful calming and comforting one, not only for him, but for us".

Education: Inside and Outside Arthur Rank House

The following is drawn from an interview with the Head of Education, Cathy Alban Jones:

What is your role as Head of Education at Arthur Rank House?

"It is a multifaceted job, dealing with the workforce both in and outside Arthur Rank House and the need for people to be educated to a specialist standard. The job also entails being responsible for the community nurses' education within the county in relation to their palliative care role. It also means that anyone facing end of life, that is anyone within the last year of their life, within a care home, also comes within the remit".

Additionally, Cathy Alban Jones is responsible for students coming to ARH. These include medical students (about 300 each year) who, during their three-year pre-clinical course, have one week within ARH. Similarly, there are about 80 other students: nurses, physiotherapists, occupational therapists, chaplaincy students and social workers, who also have to be found placements. They come to see what the Hospice does and how specialist palliative end-of-life care should be achieved. The length of time they spend at Arthur Rank House varies from a morning to four months.

Cathy has been in post for seven years during which the job has grown exponentially. She is the first full-time Head of Education. From being a half-time post, Cathy now finds she is running 50+ training sessions a year. "There is an unlimited need. The Government agenda is for more people to die in the place of their choice which will mean more trained staff are needed".

Cathy feels privileged to be in post. "Part of specialist palliative care is to educate. The aim is clear – 'living well – not waiting to die'". Since 50% of IPU patients go home, education focus can be on quality of life at home. Current figures show 44% of people die in a community setting: "We can influence this".

There is a clinical component in Cathy's job description. Since last year, she is just starting to claim this back by trying to do one day a week with the community team of Clinical Nurse Specialists (who used to be called Macmillan nurses) and who are based at ARH. There are five of them (equal to four full-time staff) for a population of 300,000. Each nurse is responsible for about 65,000 people and they cover Cambridge City, south of the City and north to Ely.

Cathy's Message

Education is the key to developing confidence in excellent evidence-based end-of-life care. "There is HUGE opportunity to influence how 44% of people die". Part of education is: "To open up conversation about dying, about planning for death". There's more and more thinking about planning in advance but she thinks there needs to be a huge push to promote this and also about how to interpret it on the ground. Since "dying at home" encompasses anywhere that is not an acute hospital environment, there is therefore a "huge potential" to work with residential and care homes.

"We have one chance to get this right" – she can see that the impact of education can set people thinking and developing and be more likely to try something they have not done before.

(Cathy Alban Jones was interviewed August 2012)

Education: Schools Co-ordinator

The Arthur Rank Hospice Charity has for the second time funded a project post and Jan Wilkins is the current Children and Young People Education and Project Co-ordinator. This is currently a two-day-a-week post. Part of her role is to increase and develop the education that ARH offers to teachers and support staff caring for bereaved children. She provides education sessions to staff working in pre-school, primary and secondary schools and sixth form colleges. The work has another dimension which is that of bringing primary school children into Arthur Rank House to meet patients in Day Therapy and to create art with them. The purpose is not only to bring the Hospice and local community together but, by bringing these Year 5 (9–10 year old) children into the Hospice, the aim is that they and their families will understand what a very positive place it is and will be less fearful of illness, death and dying.

Jan has set up talks for those working with the pre-school child facing loss and grief and also those working at primary school level. She will also be covering those working secondary schools and sixth form colleges. These talks have been offered within the county and to those working in surrounding counties.

In this section, we will be concentrating on her work with primary age children and their interaction with patients coming into Day Therapy.

Jan begins by going and talking to the children at their school. She talks about what it is like to be ill, they can all relate to that! Then she describes the situation when you know you are not going to get better. "Understanding that illness and death are part of life". She explains that when the children come into Day Therapy, they will be participating with patients who "may not look ill, but inside they're poorly. They are ill and they know they're not going to get better. How do you think they might feel?" The patients, who willingly participate in this scheme "are doing society a favour to enable children at an early stage to understand that death and dying are part of the circle of life, grief is a normal process".

Jan will ask the group of children if any of them have lost pets. Many will have experienced the death of a pet. She then explores with them how they missed the pet, what they remembered about their pet – "how you keep a relationship alive by remembering them". This leads on to talking about grief: "How do you feel? Could anyone say anything to help you? Could you eat your dinner?" But the children have found that life carries on, they go to school, eat, despite the pain.

With parental consent, the children come into Day Therapy in small groups of about 10–15 to work on art projects with the patients. They learn that a hospice is not just a place to die, but for patients to come to and use its facilities, see the chaplain, the physiotherapist, have a massage, eat a cooked meal and meet other patients. In Day Therapy, they might paint glass, make tiles and model animals or make puppets. Whatever they do, they are working together with the patients. As a result, one boy was heard to declare; "When I'm older, I'd really like to work here, because I care about people who are poorly". At the end of one session, three boys came up to kiss a patient and thanked her and got enveloped in a big hug. The patient said afterwards: "It meant much more to me, having a hug from a child".

Jan is very clear about the need to articulate grief. "Unless you are able to express it, it can result in unresolved grief which can be pathological. If you can get young children to be able to say, 'I'm hurting … I'm sad', they will be able to cope with their future, the inevitable sadnesses and losses in their own lives. Through the media, children face death every day. It's important for families and children to learn that grieving is normal and over time the pain lessens. It helps their emotional intelligence". The response to bringing together primary school children and patients in Day Therapy over joint art work has been overwhelmingly positive.

"Children can cope with anything provided they are given the truth and age-appropriate facts".

The Library

People who don't know what the library does sometimes remark that it must be a bit boring, just stamping and re-shelving books! But there is so much more to a health library than that.

Arthur Rank House is one of a small number of hospices in the country to have a fully functioning library and a librarian to manage it. It means we can offer a specialist service to staff and volunteers answering a wide range of enquiries, from how to find a particular book to tracking down an obscure article while researching the latest evidence on therapies or services. With the march of technology, much of what we do can now be done "virtually" which means providing a comprehensive service even to those who work at opposite ends of the county.

Variously described as "compact", "bijou", or simply very small, the library has around 1200 items in its catalogue and subscribes to 11 specialist journals, most of them in print and online so that they can be accessed by staff any time whether working at Arthur Rank House, out in the community or even at home. We also have many leaflets and books for patient information, including very well used and highly regarded activity books for children experiencing the serious illness and loss of loved ones.

So we have a part-time librarian and four enthusiastic volunteer library assistants, but what do we do?

Well, there's … literature searching, document supply and interlibrary loans, information skills training, issuing, renewing and returning books, current awareness services, cataloguing and classifying new resources, receiving journals and chasing missing issues, administering online licences, maintaining patient information resources ….! In fact, anything which involves finding and supplying information that helps staff keep their knowledge and skills up-to-date and so contributes to the high quality care that is so appreciated by patients and their families.

And that includes putting books back on the shelf in the right place so they can be found again by the next person!

(Debbie Hagan, September 2012)

Volunteers: Receptionist's Story

Earlier, we viewed a day in the life of Arthur Rank House through the eyes of Shelagh van Heerden. Shelagh remembers that when she came to be interviewed for the job of Receptionist, she was "absolutely overwhelmed by how many people smiled and said 'Hello'" and that then she really wanted the job, thinking the atmosphere "fantastic". She says: "All the staff seem to row in the same direction, all going forward".

To illustrate her comment, "The generosity of people, both in time and money, never ceases to amaze me", she recounted this story.

I will never forget one quiet afternoon about two years ago. The Out-Patient clinics had finished and there was a patient's family sitting chatting in the lounge area, having tea and biscuits. Suddenly a very small gentleman appeared in front of the reception desk and said in a very loud voice: "Excuse me luv, but who do ah speak to about donating me organs?"

Startled receptionist (me): "I'm sorry sir, I didn't quite hear what you said".

Small gentleman: "Ah said, who do ah speak to about donating me organs?"

The family over in the lounge area who had obviously heard what the gentleman said, were all looking over and nudging each other and obviously thinking: "Ooh! Let's see how she sorts this one out!"

Me: "You would like to donate your organs?"

Small man: "Yes luv, ah would".

Me: (Quick think! Who would deal with something like this? Think Shelagh! Think!) "If you would like to take a seat sir, I will try to find someone who can advise you".

Small man: "Ah don't need them anymore ya see".

Family in lounge area silently emitting a collective "Aaaaah, poor chap".

Me: (Oh poor man!) "Let me see if I can find someone who can help sir".

Small man: "Ah just want to get rid of them, they're no use to me now".

Family in lounge AND me emitting a collective emotional gulp.

Me: "If you would like to take a seat, I'll try to find someone to talk to you about this".

Small man: "Ah've got two of them ya see. The wife said she's fed up o' dustin' em and if I can't find someone who will tek 'em, then they're going to' tip".

Volunteers: Facts and Figures

The first volunteers were recruited as the Hospice opened in 1981. Currently there are approximately 300 volunteers supporting all activities of Arthur Rank House. The Charity funds the management, support and training of the volunteers who work in 24 areas of activity.

The following table is not intended to be comprehensive but, despite volunteer numbers fluctuating and some people working in more than one area, does give an idea of how voluntary activity is currently (early 2013) spread.

Task	Volunteers	Task	Volunteers
Tea Bar: weekdays	84	Flower arrangers	15
weekend	12	Shopping	3
Day Therapy	18	Painting bereavement cards	7
Creative services	5	Family Support	10
Cake bakers	6	(bereavement counsellors)	
Gardeners	12	Chaplaincy	13
In-Patient Unit	15	Shops	53
Afternoon teas	5	Drivers	30
		(for patients)	

There are several other significant areas of work where volunteers make a vital contribution. These include the home-sitting team, the hairdresser, PAT dogs, complementary therapy, Lymphoedema Clinic, administration, fundraising administrators, fundraising events and as Trustees of the Charity.

The 2010–11 Annual Report tried to put a financial figure on the volunteers' work, trying to represent their contribution in monetary terms. Using the minimum wage of £5.93 for most roles, together with the lowest market value for specialist roles such as counselling, the hourly rate averaged out at £6.08. With a baseline of 22,682 hours of volunteer time during the period calculated, the volunteer contribution to Arthur Rank House, costed in purely financial terms, came to £137,975 (note the Trustees' vital contribution was not part of this calculation).

During the period covered by that Annual Report, some volunteer contributions were expressed by a different and more vivid set of calculations:

265 volunteers, 31,863 miles travelled, 1,248 flower arrangements, 715 tins of soup bought for the patients' and Day Therapy kitchens, 78 haircuts, 11,093 cups of tea made at the Tea Bar, age 91 the oldest volunteer, age 17 the youngest volunteer!

Volunteers

Throughout the preparation of this book, we have been hearing: "Have you spoken to …?", "You ought to contact …". Nowhere are we more conscious of this than in relation to volunteers and those who have organised and supported their work. Pangs of conscience aside for being unable to name more than a handful of volunteers (and those almost randomly chosen), we are clear that, in relation to the past, present, and future work of Arthur Rank House, volunteers have been at the heart of its work and will continue to be so.

Dr Tim Hunt's reflection, "1981–2001: 20 years of caring" has already been quoted [Milestone: 20 Years on] but it is worth repeating part of that appraisal: "In the early years, some professionals looked aghast at the very suggestion that volunteers should have contact with patients". He concluded: "The important and indispensable role of the volunteers is now firmly established as their work complements that of many paid professionals. They are in their own way as professional as the rest of us, and the future is heavily dependent on the grace and goodness of our volunteers".

This assessment is as valid now as it was when he wrote it 12 years ago.

Also in reflective mood, on the point of her retirement, was Ann Challice who had been the Administrator at ARH from its opening. In 1992, she wrote: "Serious volunteering requires regular and long-term commitments of time – time that is in short supply". And it is indeed a truism that, generally speaking, it has become harder for many organisations to find volunteers in the two decades since she wrote. She went on to "thank all the volunteers for their tremendous support and hard work. Never has a request been refused; from feeding the parrot to taking a patient's slippers home when they had been left behind on the ward! I would have liked to ask for an alligator or a zebra, but no patient has ever wanted one. (So far!) Though volunteers at Arthur Rank House have not yet produced zebras, they do a truly astounding range of tasks – actions. The list seems endless but includes: sending off to the National Gallery for a reproduction print of a painting which a patient wanted to copy in oils; offering to 'baby-sit' some apple pies made by a patient when the Occupational Therapist had to leave while they were still in the oven".

There are many ways in which to try to show the part volunteers play in the life of Arthur Rank House. The Hospice is a far more complex organisation, community, than most people realise and volunteers play a vital role. As Anna-Louise Croft, Volunteer Services Manager wrote: "The breadth and depth of skills that volunteers bring to us, and the diversity which they add to our team, make them an invaluable asset without which we could not continue to support the psychological, spiritual and social needs of our patients and their loved ones". Agnes Toth, also with responsibilities for volunteers, drew attention to the fact that volunteering at Arthur Rank House "is about human relationships that create a strong sense of belonging, both in paid staff and volunteers. …I discovered that the volunteers will literally do anything, at any time, to help patients and families in those difficult times. It wasn't only their commitment that surprised me: it was their compassion, friendliness and never ceasing smiles that really impressed me". As Agnes says: "Everyone is valuable, whether they're offering every day for three months or two hours a month for 30 years!"

Volunteers are ambassadors, telling people about the Hospice and reassuring them about the work that is done at ARH. They are one of the means by which we can hope to dispel some of the fears and myths surrounding any hospice. They may also be ambassadors in a rather different way. There is a lovely story, not about ARH, but concerns a woman driver who crashed into the car of a volunteer driver. As a result of this traffic accident she became a hospice volunteer – though not as a driver!

One way in which volunteers are ambassadors was described a long time ago now in 1986, by Rosemary Watson who was then just beginning her job as Voluntary Help Organiser:

"First impressions can be very influential on long-term attitudes. I am struck by the thought that every new patient and every new relative who enters Arthur Rank House for the first time must have feelings similar to mine on that first day. It was both the welcome and the careful explanation that made me feel safe at once. The volunteer helpers have an important part to play in the impressions-forming stage. We cannot undervalue the Tea Bar, the plants, the fish tank, the doll's house, the thoughtfully provided provisions in the kitchen, and many other instances. Small things in themselves, they add up to an impression of caring welcome. I know this is true because many relatives have already told me so".

Volunteers have already been referred to, talked about, counted, "spoken" directly, but the last word in this section should go to Pam Wadham. She was already a volunteer on the Brookfields site before Arthur Rank House even opened, managing the Red Cross book trolley at Brookfields, when she was asked if she would "mind" taking it into the new Arthur Rank House. Puzzled as to why she would "mind", she was told that some people were sufficiently fearful of cancer that they would not want to go into the Hospice building.

For the past 32 years, Pam has been an Arthur Rank House volunteer. Like so many people associated with the Hospice, she is often asked: "How can you be a volunteer there?" Her answer? "If I end up in Arthur Rank House as a patient, I couldn't wish for a better place".

Shop Volunteers

In response to being asked why people volunteer to help in the Arthur Rank Hospice Charity shops, Sarah Turner, Senior Shop Manager, replied: "They volunteer for their needs as much as ours, sometimes more. They may volunteer to forget everyday life, or to keep busy, or because they like to be needed. For many of the men who volunteer, it is often because they've retired and their wives want them out of the house. For some, it may be a stepping-stone to a new career, particularly if they are out of work. Most volunteers do not have a connection to Arthur Rank House, though some do, they may know someone who has benefited from the Hospice. Some select our shops because they want to support a local charity. One person told me that she had looked at several possible charity shops, had gone down Regent Street and 'ours was the warmest!'"

For whatever reasons people volunteer, they really commit themselves and work very hard. They go above and beyond what one would normally expect from volunteers and could reasonably ask.

Sarah is conscious that her work also involves her at a very private time in people's lives which is when she is invited into their homes. These are the occasions when she helps a family in that very difficult task of handing over their loved one's possessions to be sold to raise money to support the work of the Hospice. Sarah very clearly remembers one occasion when she removed slippers from under the bed and the dressing-gown from the back of the door. Such home visits usually end with tea and cakes and a sense of relief and release that that part of someone's life has been completed.

Like so many of us associated with Arthur Rank House, Sarah feels that it is very important to try to change people's perspective on what a hospice is and does. Because of her own child, she is very conscious that it is important to start with children (see Education: Schools Co-ordinator section) so they realise that a hospice is not a horrible, scary place. "Death is part of life – it is going to happen".

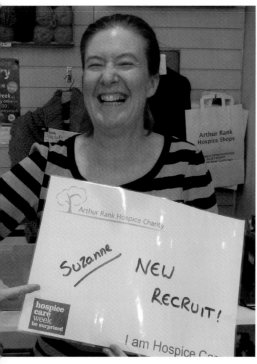

Suzanne — NEW RECRUIT!

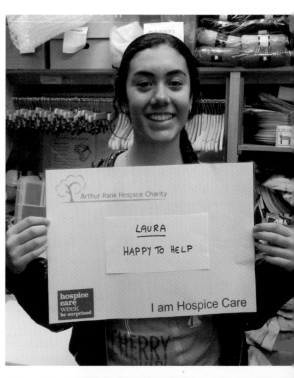

LAURA — HAPPY TO HELP

IRENE — Saturday Girl

SUE — KNITTING ADVISER

Arthur Rank House: Memories of a Volunteer

In August 1981, while the finishing touches were added to the new 24-bed unit, I rang Margaret Butchers, the cheerful and busy Voluntary Service Organiser at Addenbrooke's Hospital, who had been asked to set up the volunteers at Arthur Rank House – initially to man the Tea Bar – to see if there was any way I could help. About 10 of us were invited for a coffee, given a tour and then asked which days we were available! What a change from today! No interview, no references, no forms of confidentiality to be signed – just a very warm welcome! Immediately we were made to feel a part of the team. We soon knew everyone in the building from the Medical Director to the cleaning staff. Perhaps today with all the rules and regulations and checks, I would not have been taken on!

In due course, volunteers became involved in many different aspects of the hospice. Christine McCrum, first Chairman of the Friends, together with Celia Lindsay, the Psychiatric Social Worker, were asked to set up the Family Support Group with about six volunteers. None of us were trained counsellors but with in-house training from Celia, we met regularly and shared our problems and concerns about the patients and families assigned to us. In those days, some patients stayed in ARH for weeks, even months at a time and we became close to them. We also supported the carers at home, sitting with patients while their families had a break and, where appropriate, we went alongside those who found their bereavement difficult to come to terms with. For us, it was a great time of camaraderie and belonging and feeling needed.

The volunteers on the wards were known as "Lemon Ladies" since we wore a most unattractive yellow overall – we didn't care much for the title but it seemed to amuse the patients! Our role was to help the nurses wherever we could: making numerous beds, taking the drinks trolley round at 12 noon – a popular job. We also accompanied patients to hospital appointments, being there for families and visitors, or just sitting on a bed listening to the patients' concerns and anxieties. It was humbling to have such personal stories shared with us. Frequently when nursing staff were understaffed, we were asked to help feed a patient who was unable to do it themselves and we would often come back to help at supper time too. Many patients stay in one's memory, but one in particular was Jim, a man totally disabled with Motor Neurone Disease, who came in regularly for respite care. Jim could do nothing for himself and his speech was very difficult to understand. But he had such a cheeky smile and sense of humour, everyone loved him and there were many laughs. We would come away feeling uplifted. What a gift for us.

I was Secretary of the Friends for seven years and was so fortunate to work under very committed and inspiring Chairmen – first of all, Christine McCrum, whose vision and hard work contributed so much. In those days, we didn't need a professional fundraiser: our job was to ensure that the many generous donations that came to ARH from grateful families and the community were well spent. This included the funding of specific posts such as trained Counsellors and the Voluntary Help Organiser. Dr Bernard Reiss, a GP who was totally committed to palliative care, took over as Chairman and the Day Therapy Centre is named after him. Sadly he didn't live many years after seeing it completed. The next Chairman, Ann Mathias, oversaw the fundraising and building of the Day Therapy Centre – a vital addition to the work of the Hospice.

Being a volunteer in Day Care, as it was first known, was a wonderful experience – my favourite day of the week. The staff always made us feel an equal part of the team. We cooked simple lunches, offered manicures, foot massages and helped in the craft room. But above all, we were told that our most important role was to be there as a listener, should a patient want to offload or just chat – that was number one priority. Lunch was a very special time when we all sat together around big long tables: patients, staff, volunteers, the Chaplain, and on occasion the Medical Director would join us when the smell of garlic potato wedges tempted him down the corridor! It was a time of sharing, community, friendship and offered a measure of the normality of sharing a meal that some of the patients living on their own no longer experienced. It was an escape for a little while from their illness and loneliness.

Some of my happiest and most rewarding times have been spent at ARH. I am so grateful to the many people I met there over 26 years: patients, carers, professionals and volunteers. Through them I experienced friendship, true values, laughter, kindness, great courage, selflessness, empathy, caring and a true generosity of spirit. At ARH, I was given the opportunity and privilege to share and work among those totally committed to one single aim: to provide loving support and the very best care to those who through no fault of their own were terminally ill – just as happens today.

(Helen Gardner 2011)

Shopping

Of course shops and shopping are part of the Arthur Rank Hospice Charity Finance and Fundraising and are highlighted here, not only for the contribution they make to the income of the Charity, but because they are a constant visible presence in the community. They also take up a lot of volunteer time and effort!

Facts and Figures

The first Cambridge shop opened in Regent Street in 1995.

The second shop opened in Mill Road in 2010.

Between 2007 and 2012, the shops covenanted £200,000 to the Charity.

Between 2009 and 2012, Gift Aided shop donations raised £6,000 for the Charity.

A brief history concerned with the founding of the first shop follows, together with some volunteer stories.

Establishing a Presence on the High Street

The first Arthur Rank Hospice Charity Shop opened in Cambridge in 1995 on Regent Street, next to the entrance to Downing College. This venture was made possible by Ann Mathias, wife of the then Master of Downing.

Ann had arrived in Cambridge a few years earlier, when her husband became Master. The move from Oxford necessitated her retiring from the Clinical School of Nursing there, where she had been involved in the retraining of nurses returning to work. Thinking, "I can't waste everything", she became a volunteer at Arthur Rank House and quickly became Vice-Chair of the Friends under its inspirational Chairman, Bernard Reiss.

Ann then headed the Friends' side of the joint appeal with Cancer Relief Macmillan Fund to raise £1 million pounds for a Day Centre. Ann found she enjoyed fundraising and so, after the success of the appeal for Day Therapy, she decided, "this goodwill needs to go on".

Seeing the potential of the Friends of Arthur Rank House in boosting the profile of the work of the Hospice, she realised that Downing College's building scheme with the architect Quinlan Terry represented a great opportunity. She knew that a tiny space was coming up for commercial letting. However, she managed to persuade the college to fulfil its charitable commitment by offering the space as a shop for raising funds for Arthur Rank House. She said of herself that she had "a touch of the squirrel and a touch of the entrepreneur".

The space is indeed "tiny", but the contribution has been, and continues to be, great. *(Ann Mathias, interviewed October 2012)*

Charity Shop: Memories of a Volunteer

I am an Australian and my name is Claire Layman and I think my story in Cambridge started out quite predictably. My partner was here on sabbatical and I thought, with not much forethought as it turned out, that it would be lovely to lie around and read books for five months.

Two months in, having read lots of books, scoured the museums and seen too many old buildings, I was bored to death and taking day trips to London.

My entire view of the city changed when I started work as a volunteer at the Arthur Rank Hospice Charity Shop. Here I found the real city, with a real heart. I found a myriad of other volunteers more diverse than you could imagine, all with interesting life stories and all overwhelmingly friendly and generous, and a great boss, Helen, who runs the Regent Street shop like a well oiled machine while never seeming to.

Because of the particular generosity of Cambridge people and the broad appeal the Arthur Rank Hospice seems to have throughout the local community, the Hospice shop is particularly well supplied with excellent quality clothing and more paraphernalia than one could possible imagine. It also has a very loyal band of customers. There seems to be a rather large cohort of Cambridge people who both donate and shop.

So all that is required of the volunteers is to sort, label and sell. And then sort, label and sell. On the face of it, it may not seem the most challenging or enjoyable of missions. However, Helen and my fellow volunteers make it rewarding, fun, interesting and worthwhile.

I leave this week with the following, I imagine, report card from Helen: "B+. Prompt, reliable but constantly distracted by buying things in the shop for herself. Might have achieved an A, if it hadn't been for the worst window display ever produced in the history of the Hospice".

I leave this week to return home with one regret; not having joined earlier.

(Claire Layman, March 2013)

Unexpected Encounters

....

Sarah Turner, as Senior Shop Manager, writing about the Charity shops in the Annual Report 2011–12, described the job of being a volunteer in the shops in the following way: "There's never a dull moment as you never quite know what's going to come through the door".

The following encounters prove her point.

Five metres of heavy black and white striped cotton material had been offered for sale for some time when a lady bought it. As she was leaving, she casually explained that she needed striped material like that to make trousers for a stilt walker.

Calling out to a volunteer to look in the back of the shop – "Do we have any plain white sheets?" Success. Another explanation by the purchaser as she paid: "I want this for part of an assault course I'm making for a five-year-old's birthday party at the end of this week".

A desperate last-minute purchase – a pair of long white evening gloves, dating from the 1970s probably, for a black tie event that evening. Mention of the "black tie" resulted in our producing two bow ties to choose from. A couple happily kitted out for an evening's entertainment ensued.

Not all purchases fall into the category of last-minute acquisitions. A customer bought a lot of handbags and explained that they would be passed on to a friend who sold them to provide money to buy food for those in need in Africa. The customer explained that a relative had been cared for during their last eight days in the Hospice. In response for that care at the end of life, another relative had run a marathon and raised £1,000+ for the Hospice; "we have a soft spot in our hearts" for Arthur Rank House.

Not all would-be customers are successful. A woman came into the shop in response to a display of cookery books, but was about to go out empty-handed. She explained she wanted a recipe for pesto but, since she spent part of each year living abroad, the required recipe was in another country. The shop volunteer she was speaking to said she herself made pesto and could probably remember the recipe well enough to quote the necessary quantities – the problem that was exercising the customer. It was agreed that the customer would return after completing some shopping and that the hand-written recipe would be waiting for her – it was. Though no purchase

was made, the presence of the shop on the High Street certainly both raised the profile of the Hospice and the charity. The volunteer acted as ambassador, as so many volunteers consciously feel they are.

A shop volunteer, seeing a rug-making kit that had been donated and was on display, was moved to remember her past. She said she was left-handed and when her right-handed husband was courting her, they spent many hours making a rug. They could sit side-by-side on the sofa, each working comfortably from their respective end. Meanwhile his mother sat opposite, keeping an eye on them!

The generosity of our donors means there's never a dull moment in the shops. Volunteers say it's like a perpetual Christmas, unwrapping donations and never knowing what you will get! Offered donations have included a real live kitten, a bullet-proof jewellery counter and a grand piano. The last two we had to decline due to lack of space and the fact they would have needed a forklift truck to move them, and the owner of the kitten found it a home with her next-door neighbour!

Each year, at a convention of Charity shops from various charities across the country, there is a competition for which shop has received the strangest, most curious, donation. The picture below shows the donation on which rest the hopes of our two shops for the forthcoming year's competition.

A Special, Treasured Place

....

"It's only when something really bad happens (death, illness, disaster, dementia – something life-altering that money can't solve) that you are tipped from your comfortable, complacent rut and land in the parallel world. This is the one that's been there all the time, full of good anonymous people who, when you need them – and you never know when you will need them desperately – will help you without judgement or hesitation and with unfathomable kindness."

(Melanie Reid, a journalist, broke her neck and back in a riding accident, The Times, 3 March 2013)

What have the "Voices" been telling us about Arthur Rank House?

They speak of:
> giving life in the face of mortality;
> everybody being treated as a whole person;
> being given space and time and being listened to;
> support for patients, families and friends, and for staff and volunteers;
> sharing confidences; and everything going towards
> "making every moment count".

At the beginning of the book we said we would be celebrating Arthur Rank House through "Voices", and so, fittingly, we end with such a voice.

(Judith Chisholm, April 2013)

My Experience of the Arthur Rank Hospice

During the period that my mother was there, in December 2000, the Arthur Rank Hospice gave me and my family a total, intense sanctuary. We would emerge from a heart-rending day at her bedside onto Mill Road as though arriving in a parallel universe, one of the bustling, banal normality of traffic and shopping from which we had briefly, but completely, disconnected.

The serenity of the Hospice enveloped us, working its magic in allowing us to come to realisations not reachable in the outside world. When my mother was first admitted, ostensibly for respite care, I was still sure that if I could just find the right tasty morsel, the right recipe that she used to like, I could persuade her to start eating again. It was only after a day or two that I started to take in where we were headed, when I innocently asked how they handled people who couldn't eat and a doctor gently pointed out, "We're not in the business of prolonging life here". And that was the most important thing for my mother: I believe it was such a relief for her to be somewhere where this was accepted, that you could see her visibly relax and let go. To such an extent that she was, in fact, able to die peacefully within a week – on Christmas Day – as she wished.

I was able to have some important conversations with my mother during those few days. Typical of the support offered, my children, toddlers at that stage, played quietly with the toys in the foyer, fully aware of the gentle privilege of being there. The volunteers, sensitive to our dazed and fragile state, made my husband, brother and me many cups of tea. We took turns to sit with my mother, quietly reviewing times past and future, all matters of loss and forgiveness duly addressed.

The Hospice counselling after my mother died gave me insight and courage to re-engage. And also to deal with the immediate onset of cancer in my mother's closest friend, for which, bewilderingly and cruelly, in the irrational way of such illness, she blamed my mother entirely. I really needed support to negotiate this toxic minefield and am indebted to Arthur Rank for providing it – humanely, with care and kindness.

(Jane Kershaw, April 2013)

Acknowledgements

It is both a difficulty and a pleasure to complete this book with the proper acknowledgements. It is a difficulty because so very many people have helped, knowingly and unknowingly, in the creation and success of Arthur Rank House and the Arthur Rank Hospice Charity over the past 30 years, as well as enabling this book to have been written, that it is impossible to do justice to their generosity, commitment, support and hard work. It is also a pleasure for me to acknowledge the privilege it has been to have undertaken this project, even though I had absolutely no intention of writing a book when I answered Lucy's request, roughly a year ago, for editing help!

Several people helped give an insight into the early days of Arthur Rank House, including Sheena Henderson, Kathy Hines, Celia Lindsay, Janet McCabe, Ann Mathias, Ann Murray, Pat Owens, Doreen Rees, Esmee Young and especially Christine McCrum. Indeed, many more people have expressed a willingness to engage with this project, to share their memories, time and experiences than it has been possible to use directly – so my gratitude and apologies if you can see no direct reference to your input, but it has been much appreciated and has helped educate and illuminate this project.

I have read the Friends' Newsletters, together with Annual Reports of the Arthur Rank Hospice Charity for the last three years, and have used these as the source of passages quoted in the book unless otherwise stated.

There are, however, some people whom I wish to mention for the particular help given to me personally: Judith Braid for reading and rereading the manuscript and, in the process, saving me from at least some of the infelicities of expression and many typos, and generally going beyond the call of friendship. Chris Cook for agreeing to read a last-minute manuscript just before she was running a Jumbalance trip, so putting at my disposal the wisdom and experience gained over many years of working in a hospice and as a Marie Curie nurse. Michael Chisholm for unfailing encouragement, total support, and giving up the dining table for the four months of writing! Lynn Morgan for giving me my head, but always being there to make contacts on my behalf, get access, solve problems and always with the utmost efficiency, support and a light hand. Lucy Day as the generator of the original idea in 2011 for a history of ARH in its 30th year, for resurrecting the idea last year and accepting its change to a celebration book as well as running with the project after leaving her post. John Marshall for starting the interview ball rolling in 2011. Annie van Heerden for joining in with the project, putting her personal experiences and on-going commitment as a volunteer with ARH, as well as her publishing knowledge into "the pot". Dr Margaret Saunders for an inspiring interview and for her on-going support. I should also like to thank Stuart Evans, the current Chair of the Arthur Rank Hospice Charity, for giving me the time to explain the present organisation and for backing this project. Tiina Rajamets for her work proof reading the manuscript. Geraldine Woods as an understanding designer who used her skill and experience to combine these words and images. And, as will have been seen, there are all those who were contacted and spoke freely, sharing their work and passion about Arthur Rank House, and helping to explain and celebrate what goes on in a modern hospice and how it works in the community.

(Judith Chisholm, April 2013)